MW00641324

Once Upon a Time in

ENTREPRENEURLAND

A Collection of Entrepreneurially Positive Fables

Some True . . . Some Not So True

BY

Steve Distante

Once Upon a Time in Entrepreneurland

Copyright © 2023 by Steve Distante

All rights reserved. No part of this publication may be reproduced, stored in a retrieval system, or transmitted in any for or by any means, electronic, mechanical, photocopying, recording, or otherwise, without written permission of the publisher or author, except for the use of brief quotations in a book review.

Although the author and publisher have made every effort to ensure that the information in this book was correct at press time, the author and publisher do not assume and hereby disclaim any liability to any party for any loss, damage, or disruption caused by errors or omissions, whether such errors or omissions result from negligence, accident, or any other cause.

Adherence to all applicable laws and regulations, including international, federal, state and local governing professional licensing, business practices, advertising, and all other aspects of doing business in the US, Canada or any other jurisdiction is the sole responsibility of the reader and consumer.

Neither the author nor the publisher assumes any responsibility or liability whatsoever on behalf of the consumer or reader of this material. Any perceived slight of any individual or organization is purely unintentional.

The resources in this book are provided for informational purposes only and should not be used to replace the specialized training and professional judgment of a health care or mental health care professional.

Neither the author nor the publisher can be held responsible for the use of the information provided within this book. Please always consult a trained professional before making any decision regarding treatment of yourself or others.

To request permissions, contact the publisher at publish@joapublishing.com or steve@pitchology.ai

Hardback ISBN: 978-1-961098-34-3
Paperback ISBN: 978-1-961098-30-5
eBook ISBN: 978-1-961098-31-2

Printed in the USA.
Joan of Arc Publishing
Meridian, ID 83646

www.joapublishing.com

Dedication

To my tribe . . . This book is dedicated to you: the entrepreneur, the unemployable, my people—those who are willing to risk it all for the benefit of themselves and others. Even in the darkest hours, you possess the energy, drive, vision, courage, and insanity to muster the optimism to carry on. I am infinitely inspired by you, which I hope is evident in these pages.

To Heidi, the most amazing and important Who[1] in my life! You complete me, my sentences, and my world. I Love you!

To my dear children, Elizabeth and Quinten, thank you for making the world a brighter place and sharing your adult journey with me and Mom! We love you.

To my coaches and mentors today and over the years, especially Lee Froschheiser, Lou Grassi, Dan Sullivan, Peter Diamandis, and Joe Polish: thank you for sharing your wisdom and guidance.

Table of Contents

Welcome to Entrepreneurland

> *"When something is important enough, you do it even if the odds are not in your favor."*
>
> **—Elon Musk**

Welcome to *Entrepreneurland,* a series of fourteen true (and not so true) entrepreneurial fables through which we can relive our early days as entrepreneurs—only this time, armed with the knowledge and experiences we have today.

Yes, you read that right: fables, like Aesop (or, in this case, ESOP . . . but we'll get there).

The idea for this book came to me while I was mulling over some ideas that I think all entrepreneurs ponder from time to time, mainly:

What would I do differently if given the chance to hit the "redo" button on my entrepreneurial journey?

What industry would I venture into?

What mistakes would I be able to avoid?

How fast could I scale and grow?

Understandably, these types of hypotheticals lead to some magical thinking. But once my entrepreneurial brain kicked in, I realized it doesn't *have* to be magical thinking if I could make it reality. All it takes is a little money, the will to mentor, and a coachable entrepreneur to make the magic happen. And voilà, I got the idea for *Entrepreneurland*, both the book that you're reading right now and the network it corresponds to: the Private Investor Network.

The Private Investor Network (PIN) is an alchemic playground for both seasoned entrepreneurs ready to invest in new ideas and relatively new entrepreneurs who have the ideas but need capital. The PIN is a community where experienced entrepreneurs get the chance to play the ultimate game of entrepreneurship with a live business by investing in fellow entrepreneurs. On the flip side, investable entrepreneurs will be able to find experienced entrepreneurs to back their businesses. Basically, I created the PIN to make the painful process of raising capital and tracking those investments easier on everyone.

Entrepreneurland is a sequel to my first book, *Pitchology, The Art & Science of Raising Capital,* which is a comprehensive guide to planning and executing a fundraising strategy. *Entrepreneurland* is also a manual of sorts for the Private Investor Network. But doesn't the word "manual" make it sound boring? It's not! I've gone to great lengths to make this book as readable as possible for entrepreneurs.

Believe me, I'm well aware of the entrepreneurial inclination to be distracted by shiny things! It's the story of my life, at least until I learned how to harness my entrepreneurial drive and work *with* my tendencies rather than against them.

Friends, Romans, Countrymen: Lend Me Your Ears

If you don't know me already, allow me to introduce myself. I'm Steve Distante, your author of—a.k.a. your *author*ity on—all things entrepreneurial for this book. It is my absolute pleasure to address my community in this format. My brain is always looking for ways to create something new and exciting, combining existing concepts with new ones to create magic. Weaving the lessons I've learned—after decades of entrepreneurship—into fables has been a fun and educational experience.

I was born an entrepreneur to the point that I couldn't hear the rest of the world because I was focused on creating something new and better—doesn't everybody do that? Since you're reading this book, you can probably relate. As an entrepreneur, I identify with both Elon Musk and Albert Einstein. I relate to Elon's social awkwardness, his willingness to take risks for the benefit of others, his playfulness with things like Easter eggs (you'll see plenty of those in the pages ahead), and his habit of dreaming exponentially. As for relating to Einstein, I believe we are all geniuses at something, and it is our job to find out what that is. I found that my personal genius is a combination of my ability to think in numbers, quantify calculated risk, and scale exponentially.

If it hadn't been for the other entrepreneurs in my life—the ones like Elon Musk who inspire me in real-time and the ones who have made up my immediate community, like my mentor Lou Grassi (years ago) and my fellow EO members—I'm not sure I would have ever been able to recognize my personal gifts. This deep respect for my community is a big reason I was compelled to start the PIN and write this book in the first place.

I love entrepreneurs as much as I love *being* an entrepreneur. I am infinitely fascinated by the way our minds work. I celebrate our innovation and our appetite for risk. However, I'm also aware of the challenges the entrepreneurial nature poses to a person's life and career. The learning curve to get to a place that's stable and successful is often tough. The path can be lonely. Often, as entrepreneurs, we get in our own way and, instead of letting our companies grow, we sabotage them by becoming arsonists who continue to put the company in jeopardy just so we'll have the opportunity to save it.

Through the PIN and the stories in this book, I hope I'm able to simplify this process for some of you, no matter where you are in your entrepreneurial journey. It is my honor to guide you through this series of fables to share tales of entrepreneurship through the medium of storytelling.

Gather 'Round the Fire

Why fables?

First, people love stories. Before writing existed, that's how wisdom was passed from one generation to the next. When we read or listen to a story, we're hardwired to at least *try* to put ourselves in the character's shoes. In a similar way, we're more predisposed to remembering a story than we are to remembering facts and tables.

The second reason I wrote this book of fables is that, as I thought about the grand takeaways I wanted my readers to get from this book, I couldn't stop imagining characters, both fictitious and real, playing out the scenarios.

I started thinking, *wouldn't it be cool if I wrote a collection of entrepreneurially positive fables that perfectly conveyed the main takeaways from decades of living and working as an entrepreneur?* And because I spoke the magic words "wouldn't it be cool if?" I present to you: *Entrepreneurland.*

Fair warning: while some of these fables contain real historical events or people, they have come mainly from my imagination. In most cases, I leave it up to you to determine where my imagination takes the reins.

Chapter One

Stone Soup in Elfish Town

> *"I've actually realized a lot of people's business models are just stone soup. They never show up with anything, not even the willingness to work all that hard. They're just hoping that someone throws in money."*

—Joe Polish

Two weary carpetbaggers, Jack and David, were walking down a dirt road when they came across a sign that read: "Elfish Town, .2 miles."

They couldn't believe their luck. Where they came from, ELF* was a mindset that meant "easy, lucrative, and fun." It *had been two days since they'd last eaten. Just as they were starting to worry that the sun would set on another day without food or shelter, they were going to be surrounded by an ELF community.*

They headed up the road to Elfish Town, the vigor in their steps renewed.

When they arrived at the town square, they looked around in disbelief. Elfish Town was in shambles. Shutters hung haphazardly from the windows on all the houses. The square was overgrown with weeds. There were boards across all the shop doors.

"Does anyone live here?" asked Jack.

"I think so," said David, just as a woman in the house in front of them hurried to close her curtains.

"What do we do?" asked Jack.

"Let's do what we do best," said David.

The two men sat in the square and unpacked their meager bags. David collected dry wood and Jack started a fire.

A resident of Elfish Town approached. "You can't have a fire here," he said, his tone gruff and unfriendly.

"But where else will we cook your stone soup?" Jack asked.

David held up a round stone for the man to see.

"Stone soup?" the man asked.

"Oh yes, it's our specialty. We're traveling chefs, you see," David said.

The man eyed the fire and the two small bags. "For traveling chefs, you don't seem to have much with you."

"That's the magic of stone soup. We make it out of nothing but a stone," Jack said.

"Say, mister, you don't happen to have a big copper pot we could boil it in, do you?" David asked.

The man's eyes flashed with anger. "What makes you think you can come to Selfish Town and use my things?" he yelled.

His voice echoed off the sad, sagging buildings of the square. A woman poked her head out of a window. "Clint! What are you yellin' about?"

"These two wanderers are trying to steal our copper pot!" Clint shouted back. "Lock the door, Ellen!"

When Clint turned back to David and Jack, both of the men were on the verge of laughter.

"Why are you laughing?" Clint asked.

"So this is Selfish Town, not Elfish Town?" asked David.

"Naw, the 'S' fell off the sign years ago."

"We don't want to steal your pot," Jack said.

"We were hoping to meet some friendly people who would create ELF relationships with us. But boy, were we wrong," David said, wiping a tear from the corner of his eye as he laughed.

"It's not funny!" said Clint.

"No, you're right, Clint, it's not funny. I can't help but notice you're pretty thin. When's the last time you had a good, hot meal?" Jack asked.

"I . . . I . . . couldn't say. And it's none of your business!" Clint said.

David shrugged. "Well, we're only visitors to Selfish Town, not residents. So we'd love to share our soup with you."

Clint scowled. "How much does it cost?"

Jack said, "If you let us borrow your pot, you can eat for free."

Clint considered this for a moment. It was clear he was skeptical, but his hunger was stronger than his skepticism. He stomped across the square and back to his house.

A few minutes later, Clint returned with a big copper pot. David filled it with water from the pump in the square. They hung the pot over the fire, and PLOP, David dropped the stone into the water.

"How long does it take?" Clint asked.

Jack looked around the square, where he saw several people watching from their windows. "Probably a bit longer than it did in Sugartown, but not too long now," he said.

A woman and child approached. She, too, scoffed at the communal soup, but her child pulled at the hem of her skirt.

"You all look hungry," said Jack.

"All we've eaten for weeks is carrots!" said the child.

Jack said, "Oh, so that's why your skin is so orange!"

David elbowed Jack in the side and said, "Well, I'll tell you what—if you'll bring some of those carrots to put in the soup, you can eat the soup for free."

"I didn't grow my own carrots to give them to you!" shouted the woman.

Clint cleared his throat. "I lent 'em my pot . . . and Susan, you really are looking orange too. Maybe it's time to eat something else."

The woman looked shocked. She opened and closed her mouth several times, maybe trying to protest, but no words came out. She and the child went back to their house and returned a few minutes later with a bunch of carrots.

This process repeated a few times. Each neighbor was aghast at the idea of sharing, but eventually, the pot teemed with celery, potatoes, carrots, spinach, and someone even brought some chicken. As the soup simmered, Jack and David watched the neighbors go from standing with their arms crossed to visiting with one another.

"Oh, I had no idea your mother was sick. Shall we take her a bowl of stone soup?"

"You know, I think we could part with some of our pickled beets from last winter. We just didn't go through them."

"I heard the grocer up in Sugarville is hiring. Have you gone in there?"

"I can help you fix that broken shutter, don't you worry."

In the light of the flames, Jack and David smiled at each other. Success.

Clint was last in line for the soup. He looked into the pot and breathed in the delicious aroma of a warm meal. "Stone soup, huh?"

"We told you it was magic," David said, and winked.

"You two came here with nothing but a stone, and now we're all together for the first time in years," Clint said, "some of us eating for the first time in days."

Jack said, "We may not have resources, but we're pretty resourceful."

David said, "And none of this would have happened if you hadn't loaned us the pot. So Clint, thank you for believing in us."

Clint realized he hadn't been thanked in years—because he hadn't helped anyone in years. But hearing the words and knowing that his contribution played a part in the success of stone soup, and resulted in a warm meal for everyone he knew, brought tears to his eyes.

He looked at Jack and David. "You're welcome," he said.

Jack scooped a big ladle full of soup into Clint's bowl.

Jack and David looked around at the people of Selfish Town, communing together for what appeared to be the first time in years.

"We really made something, Jack," said David. "We created something from nothing."

"And it was a lot more than soup," said Jack. "This place will never be the same."

Jack and David were so fulfilled after their experience in Elfish Town that they decided to start their own company where they traveled from town to town, opening community centers.

As for Elfish Town, Stone Soup Day became an annual holiday where every resident made a communal meal in the square. But they felt the benefits of Stone Soup Day all year long.

Oh, and you read that right—they voted to leave the 's' off for good.

Are You Living in Selfish Town or Elfish Town?

If you're an investor, have you ever looked at an entrepreneur's pitch, seen the value in it, and invested in them, only to find out that your involvement ends as soon as the money has changed hands? How frustrating (and frankly, demoralizing) is that? You feel like an OPM (if you didn't read *Pitchology,* that stands for "other people's money") dispenser, which isn't what anybody wants.

If you're in the phase of your entrepreneurial journey where you're pitching to potential investors, do you just wish you knew the right people who could not only help with the monetary aspect of pitching but also plug you into their network and offer you sage advice about difficult situations?

If either of these descriptions sounds like you, you aren't alone. When it comes to the entrepreneurial journey, it's the tale as old as time, so to speak. But don't worry. Just as you're not alone in experiencing these frustrations, you're also not alone on the other side of them. Quite the opposite: on the other side is Elfish Town, where you'll find a flourishing community of entrepreneurs who understand each other and have each others' backs.

Speaking of amazing communities, I have to give my friend Joe Polish credit for the inspiration behind this book. Joe is one of the most supportive and generous humans I know. He is the founder of Genius Network*, of which I am a member. The Genius Network* fosters a culture of kindness and connection. Joe is an expert at creating and tapping into networks that expand expertise in business and in life. As if he weren't far enough away from Selfish Town, he's also the author of the amazing book *What's in it for Them?* And to give credit where credit is due, Joe is also the person who coined the ELF acronym of Easy, Lucrative, and Fun. When I launched *Pitchology,* Joe mentioned that he had invested in dozens of private deals and found them impossible to track and evaluate. He was thinking about stopping investing in any future deals because they are the opposite of ELF—they were what Joe calls HALF*: Hard, Annoying, Lame, and Frustrating.

Of course, the stone soup made in the story is a different concoction than the stone soup Joe mentions in our conversation. Joe mentions a scenario that plays out all too often: an entrepreneur with a pitch deck that amounts to nothing, hoping an investor will give them money and then do all the heavy lifting too. But our conversation got me thinking about ways in which the stone soup story could be an entrepreneurially positive fable as long as the resourceful entrepreneurs actually *made* something with the investment.

And that's exactly what the PIN aims to achieve. Let's dive into exactly what we can accomplish when we come together to invest in each other.

Work, Effort, and Resourcefulness: the Ingredients to Stone Soup that Investors *Want* to Eat

When I first had the idea for the PIN, I knew I wanted to include Joe Polish in a bigger way than making an Easter egg out of his ELF acronym. During the writing of *Entrepreneurland*, I called upon several of my friends who are experts in different fields so I could weave their unique knowledge into these stories. Throughout this book, you will find QR codes at the beginnings of the chapters. Scan these codes to gain access to the deeper conversations I had with other members of my community and to explore the topics covered in the fables.

Joe and I had a conversation in which we discussed the benefits of having a network and getting to do your Life's Work, what we look for in investable entrepreneurs, and much more. Scan the QR code to access the entire conversation. Here are a few takeaways:

- **Don't bullshit people.** The "stone soup" Joe Polish was talking about in the quote that opened this chapter is about entrepreneurs pitching an empty idea, clearly expecting the investor to actually do the important work. Your reputation will travel in this community, so you need to build that reputation on honesty and respect. Have the wherewithal to do what you say you're going to do.

- **"The life of an entrepreneur is a bit of a mixture of a comedy, a drama, a love story, a horror show, and everything in between. That's not an excuse to be a raging asshole." —Joe Polish**. That was worth the direct quote, I think. And Joe's right. Whether you consider yourself a "human doing," a human being, or a cyborg, you have to be genuine and respectful when asking for (and dealing with) OPM, especially when working with an Entrepreneur Investor.

- **You don't need to be the smartest person in the room if you're in a room where everybody is getting smarter**. This is the premise of the Genius Network, but it transfers to entrepreneurship in general. Oftentimes young entrepreneurs get caught up in their egos and want to be the smartest person in the room, but believe me, if you're the smartest person in the room, you're in the wrong room. We learn by watching each other, taking advice, and being humble.

- **Is the juice worth the squeeze?** Joe and I talk about how even if you don't like someone, you can still make money with them, but as you mature and evolve as an entrepreneur (and as an individual), at some point, you have to ask yourself if the juice is worth the squeeze. One amazing thing about entrepreneurs is that we are *always up to something*. So you don't have to jump into bed with the first entrepreneur who has a great idea. If you know where to look (say, the PIN), you're bound to find someone who has a great idea *and* with whom you'll enjoy doing business.

Chapter Two

The Magic Equation

$$E \times E \mathsf{I} = E^2$$

or

Entrepreneur x Entrepreneur Investor = Exponential Possibilities

This is the equation that inspired this book and platform, and I'm entirely sure it's magical. You'll see what I mean after you've read the fables. Speaking of fables, we're going to take a quick break from storytelling so I can introduce some key vocabulary that will help you going forward. Then it will be back to your regularly scheduled programming for the rest of the book.

Let's look at the magic equation of $E \times EI = E^2$.

E is the Entrepreneur. EI is the Entrepreneur Investor. The exponent is important because when done correctly, this equation leads to exponential growth. There's an exhilarating "next level" for entrepreneurs who invest in other entrepreneurs. On the flip side, when it's not done correctly, these investments can be terribly disappointing.

My BHAG (Big Hairy Audacious Goal)[‡], for this movement is to create the world's largest community of Entrepreneur Investors (EIs) to fund and advise worthy Entrepreneurs (Es) to grow exponentially. Throughout this book, I'll be referring to an Entrepreneur Investor as an EI and an Entrepreneur as an E.

But, not just any two people can come together to create magic. It's not that simple. There are certain qualities in both the EI and the E that make for especially positive combinations.

What Makes a Great EI?

Being an EI means so much more than simply making a monetary investment. Anyone with money could just throw money at a problem. But not everyone with money makes a great EI.

Being an EI is about creating expectations, accountability, and more importantly, fun. EIs can enjoy themselves while being able to help others because mentoring others is part of what it means to "give back" to our community. In the "Stone Soup in Elfish Town" story, Clint was an accidental EI when he loaned Jack and David a copper pot. The reason this worked so beautifully was the credibility this action brought Jack and David in the eyes of the other residents of Elfish Town. If Clint's investment hadn't come along with immediate community connection, the three men would've been staring at a pot of boiling water with a rock in it.

The E alone could never buy the level of experience, connection, and credibility that the EI brings to the table. The EI is a seasoned veteran of entrepreneurship. A great EI is like a ninja inside of somebody's business, where just a two-millimeter shift to the left or right can make a huge difference in that business's outcome.

A great EI:

Shares valuable insight

Beyond financial stability in the form of investments, some things an EI might provide their E include the following:

- wisdom from lived experiences

- industry contacts

- tactics to scale and grow a company

- credibility when looking to raise capital

Understands entrepreneur psychology

Entrepreneurs are often people who are not willing to listen to others. The EI understands this because chances are, the entrepreneur is a lot like a younger version of the EI. In Entrepreneurs' Organization, mentors adhere to the Gestalt Protocol, which entails sharing experiences rather than "shoulding" on others. Entrepreneurs don't like to be told what to do, so EIs almost never start a sentence with, "You should . . ." Great EIs share their experiences and let the E draw their own conclusions.

Creates and maintains a harmonious relationship

Before the company can scale, before new ideas can be explored, before the EI can plug the E into their existing network, there has to be a harmonious relationship. *That's* actually where the extraordinary value happens between an EI and an E.

Yes, *between*. This is not simply about creating growth opportunities for the E. This relationship is gratifying for the EI as well. The EI has the opportunity to change another person's life for the better.

What Makes a Great Investable E?

Throughout the conversations I had with my friends and members of my community while I was writing this book, we all discussed the green flags that tell us someone is worth investing in. Some of the qualities we look for are as follows.

A great E:

Is a kind person

An E's character matters as much, if not more than, their idea. You can have the best idea in the world, but if we're at dinner and you are rude to the server, it's over. Not only is someone being rude to the server inappropriate, but it indicates an E who is bound up in their ego to the point that they won't be coachable.

Is trustworthy

Think about it—they're asking for *a lot* of OPM in some cases. Nobody wants to throw fistfuls of cash into the garbage disposal. EIs want to invest in someone who does what they say they're going to do.

Has some semblance of a plan

It doesn't have to be a detailed roadmap for the next 20 years (most people don't have that, trust me!) but an EI wants to see something more substantial than word-and-number salad on a slide deck. We know when we're being bullshitted. If you're unclear about how to create a solid pitch, I'll direct you to my first book, *Pitchology: The Art & Science of Raising Capital for Entrepreneurs*, which is all about demystifying the art of raising capital.

Sells the *right* kind of stone soup

If you're selling stone soup in the sense that you expect an EI to do all the heavy-lifting, we can sense that. However, if you're selling stone soup and have a plan to gather all of the resources, there's a good chance you're planning to make something out of nothing, which is something entrepreneurs do exceptionally well.

Exponential Power of Life's Work

Part of my desire for the PIN is for it to function somewhat like the copper pot in "Stone Soup in Elfish Town"—the actual place in which the ingredients come together to become something. That something can be a cool project that stimulates the E and EI for a certain amount of time, maybe makes them some money, and then they get out. Sometimes, though, the type of work they do together is on a different level.

An important feature of the exponent in the $E \times EI = E^2$ equation is that it doesn't purely refer to monetary success, although that is certainly part of the desired outcome. Part of exponential growth is the personal satisfaction that comes with finding one's Life's Work.

I rarely have to actually define "Life's Work" to anyone because we all inherently know what that is. It's not work at all. It's an internal, almost instinctual, drive or motivation. Doing your Life's Work requires a high sense of awareness; it's a manifestation of what we do and don't want. Often Life's Work is not at all profit-driven. Many people's Life's Work is for a charity or nonprofit. Life's Work is often not our final work, but one of the steps or accomplishments along the journey that allows us to climb the ladder or evolve beyond our wildest dreams.

We can't all come out of the gates and get to do our Life's Work from Day One. Usually, there's quite a bit of self-discovery and growth necessary before our Life's Work is actually available to us.

The exponent in E^2 encompasses a soul-level satisfaction for both the E and the EI because they are able to come together over a subject that matters to them—maybe something they believe can save the world. EIs often find a lot of satisfaction in funding projects that make us feel good on a soul level. Personally, I enjoy investing in the arts, whether that is indie documentary films, Broadway shows, or working closely with the person who will design the cover of this book. I'm also passionate about the environment. I've spent the past few years growing Paulownia trees—the most eco-friendly trees on the planet—at my farm in Georgia (CallyFarms.Eco). I learned about these trees while raising capital for World Tree, an organization that, in turn, works with the farmers to help the farmers create financially and ecologically sustainable farms. Farmers are about the hardest workers I know!

You can look at Life's Work as *giving back* if you want to, but Joe Polish has corrected me more than once for using the words "giving back." He resents that phrase, because, in his words: "I didn't take anything that wasn't mine!" I see what he means. I'm not drawn to my Life's Work because of reciprocity; I'm drawn to it because I believe in it!

With that in mind, I've created the PIN as a place where we invest and reinvest in our communities rather than "giving back." As such, the PIN is a community aimed at lubricating the investment that goes *into* Es by giving them a platform of logic and order, which in turn makes the EI feel comfortable investing. It's not a guarantee of success (nothing is), but it helps simplify the path.

Okay, now that we've covered some key terms, it's time to get back into storytelling mode. Refill your popcorn, get something to drink, and meet me on the next page—at the end of the fifteenth century.

Chapter Three

New World, Exponential Opportunities

"Bet big, but don't bet the kingdom."

—Lord Farquaad

In fourteen hundred and ninety-two,
Columbus sailed the ocean blue.
But before he ever set sail,
He searched for funding to no avail.

'Til he was granted every dreamer's prayer:
A pairing so potent, but just as rare.
You see, Chris wasn't just a man, but a Who[1]—
For the King and Queen did need him, too.

Christopher Columbus had already been turned down by Portugal, England, and France. He was used to rejection. He'd spent the better part of a decade seeking support for his journey, and he'd heard nothing but "no."

Of course everyone said no! He needed a large sum of money and a fleet of ships to sail into the unknown with the hopes of making landfall in India. There was a massive chance he'd never come back. As far as anyone in Western Europe knew, no one had ever crossed the Atlantic Ocean before.

But when he presented his perfected pitch to the King and Queen of Spain, Columbus had an inkling that this time, it might land.

They also said no, but in a way Columbus hadn't heard yet:

"The timing isn't right, Mr. Columbus. But your idea and your presentation have gotten our attention. As you know, Spain is currently embroiled in war. We simply do not have the money available to fund your journey. However, if you're able to wait out the war, we would be interested in speaking with you again in the future."

Columbus left the castle, feeling more disappointed than defeated. He didn't want to wait out the war. Wars could last decades! Why should he trust that these monarchs wouldn't go behind his back and send a Spaniard across the ocean instead of him?

But Columbus didn't need to worry. Unbeknownst to him, two years before, Ferdinand and Isabella had talked about trying to find an alternative trade route to the west. If Columbus had come to them then, they would've said yes in a heartbeat.

It was truly just a matter of time.

For the next six years, the monarchs thought about the passionate and driven man who had stood before them, not only willing, but desperate to take on a truly unfathomable amount of risk. They prayed another country wouldn't back him before they were able to.

In 1492, the Granada war ended. Isabella and Ferdinand called a meeting with their financial advisors. The war had been costly. The advisors were torn on whether or not to call another conference with Mr. Columbus. On one hand, if Columbus succeeded, there was a possibility that Spain would become the main hub for imports and exports for all of Western Europe. On the other hand, if the mission failed, it would literally be like throwing money into the ocean.

Ultimately, the monarchs had the final say. As the advisors left the room for the couple to confer, one of them stopped at the door and said, "Bet big, but don't bet the kingdom."

Isabella and Ferdinand knew what they wanted to do. They called another conference with Christopher Columbus, and Columbus finally received his "yes."

The rest is history. Isabella and Ferdinand's willingness to back this risky endeavor paid off (at least for Spain!). Columbus's subsequent voyages to the New World provided Spain with an influx of wealth in the form of gold, silver, precious stones, tobacco, and sugar.

~

The recipe for Columbus's success might seem simple: an E willing to do something novel and an EI willing to put money behind them. But these elements are unpredictable. Entrepreneurs, for all our appetite for risk and unlimited capacity for dreaming, can often be mercurial. How did Isabella and Ferdinand know that Columbus wasn't going to use their funding as a trampoline to instate himself as a monarch in a new land, never to return to Spain? Or claim the new land in the name of his native Italy?

Without going into the deep historical details, we can say with certainty that there were contracts and agreements involved. (The punishments for failure to comply in the era of the Spanish Inquisition may have been much more severe than anything you will ever see in a contract, but stick with me.)

The understanding of the mutual benefits of this pairing was essential to Columbus's success. So while, at face value, the recipe may simply appear to be composed of the EI and the E, there's a sometimes much-overlooked third party involved: the Memorandum of Understanding (MOU). If the EI and the E aren't on the same page, success is much harder to achieve. We could look at the MOU as the oven that turns the ingredients into something actually edible.

Let's break this recipe down piece by piece.

Columbus and Monarchs

So, let me ask you a question.

When you read that little story, did you put yourself in Columbus shoes or Isabella and Ferdinands'?

There's no right or wrong answer, but whatever you answered tells you a lot about where you are on your entrepreneurial journey. If you're Columbus, you're probably reading this book as an E. If you're Ferdinand and Isabella, you're probably reading this book as an EI. Either way, there is plenty of information here for you to learn about yourself and how to harness the other to create the best possible outcome for everyone involved.

For the Columbus:

- **An EI can help you navigate your attraction to risk.** Remember, they were bitten by the same entrepreneurial bug as you, but they have more life experience to help guide you through the journey.

- **You're going to hear "no." A lot.** Sometimes, like with Columbus, it has more to do with timing than your idea. Sometimes it has to do with your idea. Learning to discern why you're hearing "no" will serve you well.

- **Reputation matters.** The people who invest with you early on can shape your entire career. Make sure they are people you respect. Don't ask for funding from someone whose career you do not admire. Remember that *your* reputation matters, and you're building it right now.

- **Build your community *before* you ask.** As Tony Robbins says, "Proximity is power." Especially at the beginning, entrepreneurs tend to work alone. You may find that in five years' time, you'll wish you had been building community for the past five years. Even if you aren't ready to cross the Atlantic yet, you should be joining networks like EO (Entrepreneurs' Organization) and meeting the people who could eventually become your Ferdinand and Isabella.

- **"The biggest heuristic for being an entrepreneur is being unbelievably persistent." —Salim Ismail.** In our conversation (QR code in Chapter Eleven), Salim shares some truly impressive numbers about how many times the founders of companies like Skype and Google heard "no" before they heard "yes." Google was around 350. What if they had stopped at 300? At 200? At 10? It's impossible to say how many entrepreneurs have stopped too soon. It's much more possible to quantify those who *didn't* stop too soon. In the interview, Salim describes more about the "sheer gumption of not stopping."

For the Monarchs:

- **Bet big, but don't bet the farm.** This quote is sometimes attributed to Steve Jobs, but I can't find any evidence that he said it. Still, whoever came up with it was right. A risk that could put you in an endless money-eating challenge is not worth it.

- **Invest in ideas that mean something to you.** It's easy to get sucked into the story an E is pitching you. But before you get involved, make sure the endeavor or the company represents something meaningful to you.

- **Recognize your Whos[1].** There was no way Isabella or Ferdinand were ever going to get on that ship and cross the Atlantic themselves. But that didn't stop the venture because they found their "Who." As Dan Sullivan and Ben Hardy teach in their book *Who Not How[1]*, we don't need to know *how* to do something, or even be the one to do it. What we do need is to identify the right people.

- **Have an exit strategy.** Know how you will get your financial return in the future and what the goal is.

- **Talk to people.** What are others saying? If they already turned down the opportunity, why was that? You can learn a lot by leaning into your community.

- **Timing is key.** Isabella and Ferdinand had a war going on when Columbus first asked. Of course, they couldn't fund his journey then. Luckily for them, the opportunity was still there when they did have the resources.

The Memorandum of Understanding Sets Clear Expectations

The Memorandum of Understanding (MOU) sets the stage for the EI and the E to be able to live symbiotically. The EI and E need to have great appreciation for each other and create the conditions necessary for success. As such, the PIN includes an MOU builder to jumpstart this process.

During the initial interview with potential Es, the wise EI will go over many points, including transparency, vulnerability, and regular financials to keep both the EI and the E on track and in the know.

It's important to note that the MOU is a non-binding, simple way to foster understanding and agreement. However, the agreements laid out in the MOU can nicely translate into a binding contract when the time is right.

At its core, an MOU is simply a list of victory conditions by which an entrepreneur will feel fully satisfied with the relationship as intended. Quite often, two big-picture thinkers will launch into a conversation about the future. But as an EI, the scope of your participation should be set in stone before you start dreaming big.

Make these things clear from the beginning:

- Is this an advisory position?

- Is this a working position?

- How frequently are we meeting: weekly? monthly?

- How do we want to engage?

- How much time do we want to put into this endeavor?

Draft an MOU that clearly defines the following:

- the entrepreneur's engagement

- the financial reporting

- the disclosure of significant events

- the leadership

- the team

All this can be adjusted, but it's important to articulate the accountability on behalf of the entrepreneur. This memorandum can also serve as the basis of a contract if needed.

MOU Reminders

- **The relationship isn't over when the money changes hands.** Many EIs I know, including myself, have invested money in other entrepreneurs hoping to ride the wave or be part of the team, only to feel disrespected, discarded, or abandoned once we have wired the money. In an effort to give back to our fellow entrepreneurs, we often spend tireless hours offering our guidance, only to find out that none of it has been taken. Not only has it not been taken, but "accepting" our guidance was just a ploy to get us to open up our checkbooks and donate money to the Es' companies.

- **The magic link leaves no question unanswered.** Higher-level investing with an EI starts with setting the stage and expectations. At the PIN, we send a fill-in-the-blank magic link questionnaire to the E before the pitch (avoiding being "pitch slapped"!) to help us evaluate their deal. It is meant to help the EIs understand the investment so as not to interrupt the presentation, make sure the pitch is well thought-out, and the investment fits in our portfolio. The magic link asks questions such as, "What sort of investment is this? Is there an exit? What is the name of the entity?" and so forth.

- **EIs experience a different level of investing—one that's engaging, exponential, and life-giving.** EIs aren't always looking to invest solely to get a bunch of money in return. In fact, that's rarely the goal for these sorts of ventures. We want to be part of the journey and strategy. And we can make a *huge* difference. Think about it: if you're a young E with a great idea but not a whole lot of experience, an EI can provide not only funding but access to their network, experience, and an incredible amount of credibility—just because they believe in you and are involved with you.

- **MOUs set the stage for a harmonious relationship.** I am regularly brought in as a mediator for EIs and Es to try to create a more harmonious and symbiotic relationship when things go wrong, or to help identify an exit for the EI because the relationship is so painful. While I'm glad to mediate, I also see time and time again that the issues the EI and E are sparring over could've easily been agreed upon beforehand in an MOU.

Chapter Four

The Gift

> *"The greatest good you can do for another is not just share your riches, but to reveal to them their own."*
>
> **—Benjamin Disraeli**

Not so long ago lived a young man named Erik. His father was a shepherd and he expected Erik to follow in his footsteps, as he had followed in his father's footsteps, as had his father had done, as well as his father's father before him. Everyone knew that's how the world worked and always would.

Although Erik enjoyed the magical wandering of his mind during hours alone in the field, he had no desire to become a shepherd in his father's likeness. Alas, 'twas the very wandering of his mind, the thing he loved the most in this world, that had begun to stir discontent within him.

He had a dangerous thought: Must it be this way?

Erik fostered an affinity for things tiny and mechanical. At night, Erik worked by flickering flame to disassemble watches and clocks, pulling out their miniscule pieces and studying every surface and plane. He learned what made them work, what made them break, and how to reassemble them to working order. After a few months' time, he was making clocks of his own design, copying the mechanisms he had studied and exploring what he could change.

At the age of sixteen, Erik announced to his father that he planned to leave the fields to make his own way selling his clocks and watches.

"My son, I don't have to tell you this decision is foolish. The work of a shepherd has provided stability for our family for generations."

"Father, 'tis not stability I seek. It is creativity, followed, I can only hope, by reward."

Knowing he could say nothing to dissuade his son, the father relented.

A year passed and Erik rented a small store in town. His best friend became his business partner and worked the front, welcoming customers, making sales, and handling the bookkeeping while Erik repaired clocks and watches and worked on his own designs in the back room. The business grew as word spread about the quality of Erik's work.

Another year passed. Erik was happy with his choice of work, but the watches and clocks that had so fascinated him in his youth were beginning to lose their novelty. He would never tire of finding new ways to improve his designs, but the work was tedious and thankless. Erik's hands were constantly busy as he worked long, lonely hours; yet each month, his business partner reported that there was hardly enough income to cover the store's rent. While his business partner had taken a wife and spoiled her in fine clothes, Erik had not had a day outside of this store in over two years.

One day, Erik came out of the back of the shop while his business partner was ringing up a transaction for a customer. Erik saw his friend surreptitiously drop a big gold coin right into his pocket instead of into the till. At first Erik said nothing. But that night he pulled out the ledgers and discovered that his friend had stolen a significant amount of gold from the business over the past few years.

Erik lay his head on the ledger and wept. He wept for the many hours he had struggled. He wept for the betrayal. He wept in anticipation of confronting his friend—the one person he saw day in and day out. Erik found himself wishing he had his face pressed against the new wool of a lamb instead of this book of ink and deceit.

"This was all a terrible mistake!" he cried, and threw the book across the shop, where it slid across the floor until it stopped short under a large black boot. Erik's eyes traveled up from the boot to find an old man standing in his shop.

How did this man get in? The bell over the door hadn't dinged. Erik thought he was being robbed and reached for the knife he kept under the counter.

"No need for the knife, Erik," the old man said. "I'm only here to help."

"What do you mean?" Erik asked.

The old man walked up to the counter where his face was lit by the candle. There was a familiarity to his face. Erik thought perhaps it was a long lost uncle. He felt an inherent trust for the man, and softened.

"What happened, Erik?" the man asked.

"My only friend betrayed me," Erik said.

"How so?"

"He stole from me," Erik said.

The man nodded. "Tell me why your friend knew more about the finances of your business than you did."

Erik was slightly taken aback. "I'm too busy creating to worry about the numbers. I don't even know how to do it."

"I agree with you, Erik, that these are terrible circumstances. Still, we have to be sure not to blame others. You handed off your finances because you didn't understand them. If you're truly the head of this business, you cannot bury your head in the sand."

"But I know nothing of bookkeeping . . ."

"Erik, I am not telling you that you have to become a bookkeeper. I'm telling you there is a difference between delegation and abdication, and you'd be wise to learn it before this happens again."

Erik knew the man was right, even though he didn't want to hear it. With a thud, Erik sat down at his desk. "I can't believe how much money I've lost. This is a disaster."

"You've lost a sum, but you've learned invaluable lessons that take other men decades to learn. You must look at the money lost as tuition to the institution of wisdom and experience. I can tell you with certainty that this will never happen to you again."

Erik nodded. The man's words gave him confidence, but there was still pain in his heart.

The man said, "In the absence of information, we tell ourselves stories. You are telling yourself that your friend hurt you because he did not love you. But in a few years' time, you will realize that outgrowing people is a part of life, and it is certainly a part of business."

The man slid his hand across the desk. He lifted his hand to reveal a small, dull rock.

"What is this?" Erik asked.

"It's a gift," the man said.

Erik picked up the stone, which was cloudy and unattractive. It didn't look like a gift.

"Some gifts aren't obvious at first, like your friend—the thief. But I can tell you that once he's gone from your business, it will heal. This discovery, no matter how painful, is a gift."

"How did you know?" Erik asked.

"Let's just say I've been there," the old man said. "And by the time you realize the power of this gift," he gestured toward the stone, "this will all be a distant memory."

Erik didn't know what to say. He nodded, hoping the man's words were true. He turned the stone around in his fingers. When he looked up, the old man was gone.

Erik dropped the stone into his pocket. He touched it for courage when he confronted his friend the next day. He kept it in his apron as he toiled the long hours alone. He rubbed it between his fingers for luck, and over time, the stone smoothed until it was shiny. He never forgot the stranger's words, which, as it turned out, were true. After his friend's departure from the store, Erik's business did heal and flourish.

Erik realized that even though he'd been burned, he couldn't do it all alone. He hired another young man to work at the desk. He also hired a Who[1] to handle the bookkeeping. His chief of finance proved to be an amazing addition to his business, not only running the day-to-day numbers, but providing insight and suggestions for growth. While Erik trusted his chief of finance, Erik also created a system that ensured that he was, himself, always abreast of the finances and never let one single person have control of them.

A few years later, Erik bought a newspaper off the street. As he bit into his morning apple, a headline caught his eye:

Paris — Curie Brothers Discover Piezoelectricity Using Quartz

He went on to read the article, which explained that the French scientists had discovered that tiny amounts of electricity are produced by applying pressure to quartz.

Out of habit, Erik's hand found the stone in his pocket. The old man's words echoed in his mind: "By the time you realize the power of this gift, this will all be a distant memory."

Then he realized: the stone was quartz.

Erik dropped the apple onto the floor and rushed to his workshop. After many months of experimentation, Erik created the world's most accurate timepiece, which took the watch and clock industry by storm.

Erik was able to travel the world and have a family. He expanded his business many times, opening storefronts in London, Dublin, Paris, and Berlin, and his business continued to spread. His models were available at fine timepiece retailers worldwide.

Years later, when he had grown old, he looked into the mirror and saw the face of the man who visited him on the worst day of his life. He chuckled to himself.

"Thank you for helping me see the gift," he said. And he knew that the real gift wasn't the quartz itself, but the words his older self had spoken, which Erik Rolex had abided by every day of his life, and which had proven to be true in every way.

The only question now was how he was going to learn to time travel, having already mastered the art of keeping time.

The Power of Mentorship

Okay, real talk. This is not the actual history of the quartz watch. Erik Rolex is, as you probably guessed, a fictionalized character. However, the invention of quartz watches *was* an enormous advancement in a technology that had largely remained unchanged for centuries. In fact, when the Seiko Astron hit the market in 1969, it disrupted the watch industry so thoroughly that several Swiss watchmakers almost went out of business.

This fable came to me when I thought over the question, *What do I wish I could've told myself when I was at the lowest point of my entrepreneurial career?*

And the answer was actually what my own mentor, Lou Grassi, *did* tell me when I was at my lowest point: "It's going to be okay. Learn to reframe this as a gift. Keep going."

More than ten years ago, I found myself in the same situation as Erik. My best friend had embezzled money from my company and it felt like I might lose everything. I'll spare you the finer details, but believe me, I wouldn't wish that on anyone.

I turned to Lou, who helped me see past the immediate hurt. He told me my business would heal . . . and it did.

When most entrepreneurs find themselves at that career crossroads where they're wondering if they should throw in the towel, they go looking for capital and nothing else. Of course, there are problems that only immediate money can solve. But the smart entrepreneur—or maybe the one who has read this book—goes looking for a relationship beyond money.

If you're a potential EI, imagine what you would tell your former self at the lowest point in your entrepreneurial journey, or what you'd tell someone in general to help them avoid the pitfalls you learned the hard way.

Here are some of my own pieces of advice:

- **Where there's smoke, there's fire.** In retrospect, there were signs my business partner was stealing from me. Of course, I didn't want to believe it. But numbers don't lie, so remember, it's always worth double-checking if something isn't adding up.

- **Have your bank statements delivered directly to your house.** It is not *if* someone steals from you, it's *when*. The best way to not let that happen is to always stay aware of the numbers. My former business associate was very territorial over the statements and accounting in general, which was a red flag. Also, have your bank put copies of the checks that were presented during that period onto that statement. This is often a feature you have to request.

- **Get the right people into the right seats.** Just because someone is your friend doesn't mean they should be the president of your company. If your friend happens to be a great leader, that's wonderful. But I promise, if they aren't a great leader, you don't want to find that out the hard way. In *What Got You Here Won't Get You There*, Marshall Goldsmith writes about "growing out" of your team members, meaning the business has grown beyond the team members' capabilities. Be aware that this happens and know how to identify it when it does.

- **Keep an eye on how people interact with you.** Before I discovered my friend was stealing from me, he was acting strange. He was defensive in a way I'd never known him to be. He stopped looking me in the eye. My gut told me something was off, but he was always able to talk his way out of my questions. An entrepreneur's gut instinct is strong. When someone's acting weird, or you get the feeling that they're being inauthentic with you, it's worth it to find out why. Chances are, this isn't a person who needs to be handling a lot of responsibility in your company.

- **Learn to recognize a wolf in sheeps' clothing.** When my company was in peril, people came out of the woodwork to try to buy me out for a fraction of my company's value. They assumed I was desperate. When you are desperate, you'll look for lily pads you can hop to as little safety nets to keep you out of the water. Someone lowballing you like this is not a lily pad; their "offer" is a death trap for your company.

- **Be psychologically open.** These pieces of advice I'm giving are meant to help you stay diligent, not make you closed off. When your mentor gives you guidance, you need to have a certain level of openness in order to receive it. Don't miss the opportunity to gain wisdom because you think you already know best or because you're afraid to trust again. It is often pain that allows an entrepreneur to be vulnerable enough to accept guidance. If you find yourself in that painful scenario, accept the help.

Chapter Five

It Takes a Village

"Community will help you through the hardest of times."

—Steve Distante

We spent the last chapter following Erik Rolex from his first interest in working with watches and clocks all the way to being the most well-known watchmaker on the planet. Of course, when dealing with a life story in under five pages, major events and contributors are going to be glossed over.

So, if you'll indulge me in another foray into Erik's story, there is another very important visitor who comes into Erik's store not long after his older self: his mentor—a visitor whose impact on Erik's career trajectory (and quality of life) is just as influential.

~

The bell over the shop door jingled and once again, Erik had to drop his tools in the workshop and hurry to the front to greet a customer.

The customer, who wasn't much older than Erik, was there to pick up a watch he'd brought in for repair two weeks before.

"Name?" asked Erik.

"Peter Stockton," said the customer.

"Of Stockton Bookbinding?" asked Erik. He passed the shop every day on his way to work but had never gone inside. Even before his business partner betrayed him and Erik was left to cover the business alone, Erik didn't have time for reading.

"That's the one," said Peter.

"One moment," said Erik. "I'll go get your watch."

Erik returned from the back with Peter's repaired watch. "Good as new," he said, and he handed the watch to Peter.

Peter watched Erik flip through the book of receipts. Erik was visibly exhausted with dark bags under his eyes and a waxy complexion. "Where's your employee?" Peter asked. "Are you working alone these days?"

Erik sighed, ripping the receipt out of the book. "Yes. It's a long story, but yes, I'm working alone."

Peter took the receipt and dug in his pocket for his money. "If you want to tell me the story, I'll listen," he said.

Erik didn't know what to say. He hadn't spoken to anyone except the strange visitor about his friend's betrayal. In all honesty, he was desperate to talk about it. But with a customer? That seemed wrong.

Peter Stockton smiled. "I can assure you that I understand more than you may think. The first few years of Stockton Bookbinding tested me to my limit. I wouldn't *have gotten through it without the Shopkeepers' Association. We're having a meeting next Monday night. Would you like to come with me?"*

Erik thought for a second. He'd just been burned so significantly by his most trusted friend. Why should he let anyone else know anything about his business? But he saw the kind expression on Peter's face and inherently trusted him. "That sounds wonderful," he said.

"I'll come by here at 7 to walk with you," said Peter. "Thank you for restoring my grandfather's watch. It is the most precious thing I own and shall ever own. I value what you do." With that, he left the shop, setting the little bell jingling again.

The following Monday, Peter arrived at 7 p.m., just as Erik was flipping the store sign to "closed."

Together, the two men walked to the Center Pub, where, unbeknownst to Erik, the Shopkeepers' Association (SKA for short) had been meeting monthly for almost 10 years. Peter told Erik of all the ways the members of the group had helped him through the various turmoils of business ownership.

Before they entered the pub, Erik said, "I just found out my best friend, the employee you asked about, was stealing from me. And I let it go on for years because I'd just buried my head in the sand. I'm not a good business owner. You may want to reconsider if I deserve to be in this club."

Peter reached out and placed his hand on Erik's shoulder. "Believe me, Erik, everyone in here has been through that same scenario, or worse. There's a saying in the group: 'It's not if*, it's* when*, someone steals from you.' Stealing is human nature, and we must learn how to prevent it from happening. Trust me, as deceived as you feel, this discovery is a gift. Think of it as found money! I assure you, you're not a bad business owner. And we welcome you here." He pushed the door open.*

Inside, Erik found a group of people from his town and a few neighboring towns who welcomed him with open arms. They listened to his story about his friend stealing and offered him sympathy. Peter was right; most of them confided in Erik their own stories of betrayal. Some of the worst stories involved deceit by family members. After each tale of woe, everyone raised their pints and angrily said, "Beers!"

That wasn't the only conversation of the night, however. Several of them announced successes, to which all the others raised their pints high and shouted, "Cheers!"

Erik had never felt celebrated, not even by his family. He was actually surprised at the amount of support, rather than envy, that he saw. He wasn't sure he'd feel comfortable announcing a success in front of anyone after what his friend did. But as he clinked glasses with these people, he felt part of himself healing.

It was through a conversation he had with a financial advisor at the next Shopkeepers' Association meeting that Erik was able to create a system of bookkeeping that ensured a segregation of duties and allowed for transparency for all financial transactions. Under this system, Erik was not the only person in charge, but he also wouldn't lose oversight.

Over the next several years, Erik's relationships with the members of the Shopkeepers' Association flourished, even as his business expanded exponentially into other countries and markets. The people who supported him from the beginning remained his closest friends and confidants. There was nothing that inspired Erik more than the way the Shopkeepers' Association members supported each other. At times over the years, they helped each other raise money to keep a business afloat, filled in for each other if a shopkeeper was sick, and shared their experiences under similar circumstances. Sometimes they bought each others' businesses so someone could retire. And, at the very least, they were always around to lend an ear to whoever needed it.

As the years passed, Erik noticed that he had shifted roles within the organization. He still relied on his fellow SKA members for advice, but more and more, he was giving the advice rather than taking it. He enjoyed mentoring his fellow business owners to help them through their darkest of experiences. He often said, "The greatest battle you are going to have to fight is between your ears. That's why we're here—to lift one another up to get through the rough patches. Let's admit it: after getting a taste of business, we could never work for someone else and if we did, we would be horrible employees!"

Each time he said this to someone in the Shopkeepers' Association, he was met with "Cheers!"

He learned that there really were people out there who understood his drive and passion for what he did. Even after Erik's company became an international sensation, he continued to give back to his community by locating the Rolex Research and Discovery team at the very workshop he had rented as a young man. Young entrepreneurial-minded people from his hometown could apprentice under some of the brightest innovators of the time, learning valuable skills before they went out into the world to start their own companies.

When Erik was old enough to recognize his face in the mirror as the man who had helped him that day so long ago, he realized with great pleasure that even had he not had the bit of quartz, his life of work would've been just as satisfying thanks to people that were with him along the way.

Alone is Not the Only Option

Sometimes I can't decipher the difference between my entrepreneurial spirit and my introversion. They've fed each other in both healthy and unhealthy ways at times. I've always had the urge to own my own businesses, ever since I was a little boy selling horse manure to gardeners (If you haven't read *Pitchology,* you can find the whole story there!). But I was never able to scale my businesses until I had a community in place.

When I was a young entrepreneur, I found my way to Dan Sullivan's Strategic Coach[1] program, which helped me make sense of how I spend my time. There in the classroom in Toronto, I got my first taste for what it meant to be surrounded by other entrepreneurs. Before that, I'd always felt like a gorilla in a group of monkeys. No one was ever as driven as I was. People misattributed my drive as ADHD and told me I wasn't a good listener— which is kind of true, but I listened to myself usually. Because interactions with others often left me understimulated, my entrepreneurial spirit fed my introversion, and it took me a long time to find my people.

Not long after attending the Strategic Coach program, I went to "test drive" the Entrepreneurs' Organization (EO). I was hooked. They described *me*: my journey, my inner thoughts, my struggles . . . I might've been a little freaked out if I hadn't been so relieved.

EO was exactly the community I was looking for. I've been able to do things that I couldn't have even imagined without them, such as sharing the UN's sustainable development goals to solve some of the world's greatest challenges through business.

EO was the reason I got through the embezzlement fiasco with my former business associate. The other members of EO didn't judge or scold me for any mistakes on my part, but they did help me become stronger, more confident, and accountable enough that I'd never be financially abused again. My forum (a smaller unit inside of EO) helped me come up with a strategy and unwind that mess in an organized methodology.

EO helped me find my tribe—my community, my entrepreneurial family. I feel most alive when I'm communicating and collaborating with fellow entrepreneurs. And I want that for all of us so much that I'm creating my own platform to help us invest in each other.

Find Your Tribe

- **Entrepreneurship is lonely.** The textbook entrepreneur is an introvert, an outside-the-box thinker, a workaholic, and someone who might not have the best social skills. Add that to the unimaginable demand of a new business and you have a recipe for loneliness. Honestly, for a lot of entrepreneurs, being alone is probably more comfortable than being vulnerable. Many of us learn from a young age that the only people who will cheer us on are our parents, if we're even that lucky. I know countless entrepreneurs with fractured relationships with their siblings that grew resentful of the entrepreneur's success.

- **There are many ways to be part of a community.** You can join an organization like EO. You can mentor a young entrepreneur. You can be an investor. The most important thing is that you don't try to go at it alone all of the time. There is really no limit to the amount of investing we can do in each other.

- **Vulnerability and accountability are potent.** As entrepreneurs, we live in our heads. We need to let our guards down and be part of a community, even if the fellow entrepreneurs within that community are in different industries than we are. There will be wisdom and support without direct competition. Communities like EO breed self-awareness, encouraging us to take the mask off and look in the mirror. Open the kimono, so to speak. This is the only way we're able to evolve and grow.

- **Education is validation.** Education isn't exclusively limited to the classroom; it's experience, mentorship, and yes, often some training too. One of the most valuable aspects of any education is learning how to work and lead others, which can be a challenge for many entrepreneurs.

- **What do entrepreneurs do when they're done building businesses? They die.** Okay, this point is kind of bleak, but it's largely true. If we aren't creating, growing, mentoring . . . we're dead. Joining communities can add to not only the longevity of our businesses but also our quality of life. We're able to easily access people to collaborate with and who need us just as much as we need them.

- **Most businesses fail within the first five years.** Being part of a community will increase your odds of survival along your journey through the sharing of similar experiences with your peers. Survival of a business is often battled more in the space between our ears than in the business itself.

- **Community creates more sustainable businesses and happier people.** Engaging in a community is one of the healthiest choices I made. Communities teach you how to grow, how to get through challenges, and how to not feel alone.

- **Other entrepreneurs will become your family, your community.** When you're first struggling to make it happen, many people doubt you; family and friends often shame you by saying things like, "Why can't you get a real job?" Once you become successful, they then resent you. Most entrepreneurs, including me, have lost friends and family over their success. That doesn't mean you should cut off communication with your actual family once you become successful. It simply means that fellow entrepreneurs are the people who will understand you and your journey better than anyone else, and will celebrate your successes when your birth family may not.

Chapter Six

Bite < Growl < Lick

"Leadership is not about being in charge. It's about taking care of those in your charge."

—Simon Sinek

Once upon a time in the small farming village of Pigville, a dog gave birth to a litter of puppies. There were five puppies in all. Four had soft, golden fur and round, pink tummies. The fifth puppy was different. He was born with his umbilical cord around his neck and was completely blue.

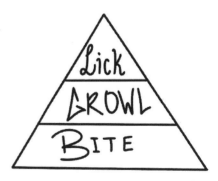

"Come on, Baby Blue," his mother prayed as she rubbed the pup between her paws. Luckily, she was able to revive him. But even as the oxygen made its way through his body, his coloration remained a silvery blue. Even though his real name was Doug, the nickname "Baby Blue" stuck, and the pup became known as B.B.

As the weeks passed, his mother feared that B.B. would grow up to become a wolf. She'd heard stories like this but had never seen it for herself. Wolves had a very bad reputation in Pigville, as well as in many other places. Pigs loved dogs, but wolves had to work hard to gain the pigs' trust.

The mother's fears were confirmed as B.B. grew. He was ravenously hungry, eating three to four times what her other puppies required. He got so big that he couldn't help but accidentally play too roughly with the others. While his brothers and sisters enjoyed the toys their mother supplied them, B.B. was never satisfied. His mother worried that B.B. would never be satisfied a day in his life.

One by one, the other puppies got adopted into families, but no one ever chose B.B. When B.B. was almost a year old, he said goodbye to his mother and trotted off to go live alone.

B.B. tried a string of odd jobs in his youth, but he was never very employable. He was too big, too scary-looking, and he almost always intimidated the boss. The truth was, B.B. hated being told what to do.

He was going to have to be his own boss, he decided.

His first business was a manure delivery service. He worked alone, shoveling manure from the cow fields west of Pigville and delivering it to the wheat farms east of town. The work was physically demanding, but B.B. would rather do this than work for someone else anyday. His reputation grew, and B.B. found himself needing to expand his work force to keep up with demand. He hired a couple of weasels to help him. Weasels also had tainted reputations in Pigville. They were silly animals who would regularly drop their shovels to wrestle each other.

B.B. had everything to lose with this business. He had no outside help, no backup plan. He tried to manage the weasels' playfulness through intimidation. When he found them tussling in the field, he was so angry that, in a fit of rage, he bit one of their tails. The weasels scurried off, never to be seen again.

B.B. stood alone in the field. Now what?

A couple of years later, B.B. was running his second business: a limo service. He acquired a used tuxedo and top hat to go along with his limousine. Business went well. He was booked almost every night between Pigville and the neighboring town of Sugarville. Best of all, one night he escorted a group of bitches (literal bitches— c'mon) to a dance, and one of them caught his eye in the rearview mirror. She asked for his business card, and a few months later they were a couple. Soon after that, they were married.

The limousine business went well. Soon enough, the demand exceeded his fleet of one. He was hesitant to hire again, not wanting to repeat the weasel fiasco. This time he hired pigs. His four new employees were reliable, happy creatures. B.B. never snapped at them. He'd learned the hard way how to control his temper.

However, B.B. ran into another problem—another part of his demeanor that he couldn't control very well. He had a family to support now, which made him ever more reliant on the business's success. He was hungry. When B.B. thought about the success he wanted to see, he would salivate and growl. Once, a pig employee came into B.B.'s office to find him daydreaming behind his desk with thick strings of saliva hanging from his jowls. The pig assumed B.B. was dreaming of a pig roasting on a spit. He spread that rumor around the office, and soon enough, all the pigs were calling B.B. "Big Bad Wolf" behind his back. After a few months, all of his employees had quit.

B.B. didn't know what to do. He thought he was doing so much better at controlling his anger by not biting, but he learned that his growling often didn't get him the results he needed. Two teams had now abandoned him. Maybe he wasn't as good at controlling his tendencies as he thought. He was learning a lesson that most entrepreneurs have to learn at some point: it's more effective to lead through inspiration than intimidation or motivation.

But . . . was B.B. himself inspired?

He looked at his fleet of driverless limousines. This wasn't what he wanted to do with his life. He was a wolf for God's sake! He wanted to do something that changed lives, and this wasn't it. He sold the limousine company and used the proceeds to start his third venture—a security company—to help Pigville overcome its rat problem.

B.B. worked alone during his first few months, then made a horrendous, yet educational, hiring mistake (which you'll read all about in Chapter Eight). *Hopefully it isn't too big of a spoiler to say that he eventually figured it out.*

A year later, business was going smoothly for the first time. Not only was there harmony within the workforce, but within B.B. as well. The company was providing a much-needed service for the town and doing well financially. B.B. felt the desire to mentor others to help them start their own businesses.

A young pig named Lisa Littlepig had recently started working in administration. B.B. saw something special in Lisa. He knew that a large part of business security was having the right people in the right seats, so he started training Lisa to take on a bigger role at the company. The mentorship was symbiotic, and through Lisa's insights, B.B. learned how to be a better leader.

He no longer snapped at, growled at, or intimidated his employees. He learned that by working in a field that fed his unique abilities[1], he no longer scared off employees by trying to motivate them.

Now, he inspired his employees through recognizing their efforts, celebrating the wins, and sharing the sweet taste of success with everyone who came together to create it.

Intimidation < Motivation < Inspiration

My friend Dr. Doug Brackmann's new book, *Wolf, Sheep, and Shepherds* (available in April 2024) likens entrepreneurs to wolves, and I can't think of a better analogy. Wolves are the villains of so much lore, yet are an incredibly vital part of many ecosystems. As an entrepreneur's business grows, they have to learn how to select and mentor the people who work with them. Often this takes a few years—

and a few alienated employees who may jump ship. The wolf has to learn how to be a shepherd, which isn't a role wolves perform naturally. As Doug explains in our conversation, there's a big difference between a shepherd standing behind a flock of sheep, driving them forward by scaring them, and a shepherd whose sheep follow him by choice.

Doug and I discuss the natural progression many leaders have to go through as they learn how to harness their "inner wolf" for good. It's easy for us to intimidate others; we have an intense presence. But as we grow, learn, and evolve, we become more effective leaders.

This evolution often follows this pattern:

1. **Manipulation.** Manipulation means using intimidating force (verbal or monetary) to reinforce the hierarchy between the leader and the employee. This is an inelegant tactic rooted in desperation and inexperience. Often at the beginning of an entrepreneur's career, they will rely on manipulation because they a) don't have a stable business yet and are therefore always afraid of failure and have a scarcity

mindset, and b) haven't learned how to effectively lead their people. They're often young and inexperienced humans in addition to being new business owners. To be frank, I'm ashamed of some of the ways I manipulated people early on in my career, and most of the entrepreneurs I talk to have similar stories.

2. **Motivation.** Like B.B., you learn that growling and snarling at others doesn't yield great results. So you manage yourself better. Still, you're just looking to feed yourself. People can hear your stomach rumbling and see you salivating with new ideas. They feel like they are the means by which you are pursuing your dreams rather than invaluable members of a team working toward a goal that's bigger than all of you.

3. **Inspiration.** The inspired leader sets the stage so that everybody wins. Inspiration appeals to a person's spirit, their intentions, and their values. This can come from a company trying to do something good in the world so the people within the organization feel like they're doing more than simply making the owner rich.

Inspiration fulfills something in people's inner world. They're inspired by the leader's drive and their ability to accomplish a mission.

As you're navigating your own journey through this pyramid, or helping an E through this process, here are some things to keep in mind:

- **Entrepreneurial drive is natural.** In my conversation with Dr. Doug Brackmann, we also discuss his first book, *Driven: Understanding and Harnessing the Genetic Gifts Shared by Entrepreneurs, Navy SEALs, Pro Athletes, and Maybe YOU*. This book's main topic is the Driven⁺: a person who is highly motivated (and often highly distracted). Many of these people have a unique genetic characteristic of having the allele (mutation) genes DRD2-A1 or DRD4-7R, or both. Our drive is in our DNA! The most interesting part is that the same allele may be responsible for other risk-taking behaviors such as addiction and some criminal acts. How you channel your energy is your choice. Left unattended or unaware, that drive can turn into negative results, but when harnessed for good, it can change the world. A Driven's⁺ energy is undeniable, and hopefully, as the entrepreneur (or E) evolves, they learn how to properly channel it.

- **Internal drive might come from different sources.** There are a lot of Drivens[+] in places of high power; some are driven by heart or by wounds, while others are driven by greed. One of my favorite things Doug Brackmann says in our conversation is that soul-inspired, manifesting people see something in the world that must be created, but there are others who have to create because they're running from fear to prove something to themselves in a narcissistic kind of investment. Doug says it takes a little fishing to see someone's soul. If you're too hasty with getting to know them, you might miss it (or they hide it *really* well).

- **Drivens[+] flock to different careers.** Doug explains that there are exceptionally high numbers of Drivens[+] who are high-performing athletes and Navy SEALS. There are also a high number of dictators who are Drivens[+]. Whether it's for the greater good or not, a lot of Drivens[+] are on the edge of being superhuman. A Driven[+] might be attracted to more than one outlet for their energy. It would not be unusual for Drivens[+] to be attracted to extreme sports, fast driving, and jumping out of perfectly good airplanes just to get a jolt of adrenaline.

- **Don't try to figure out what inspires people. Hire to it.** This was an enormous breakthrough for me. Don't try to change someone's values. Part of surrounding yourself with the right people is finding those whose values already align with the organization and its mission.

- **A leader learns to stand in someone else's shoes.** This is another gem Doug drops in our conversation. He says that inspirational leaders learn to put themselves in someone else's position and to lead them from that person's point of reference. Evolved leaders understand that what inspires *them* might not inspire other people. You have to get to know your team.

- **Learn to become a servant leader.** The act of giving releases serotonin, oxytocin, and dopamine for everybody involved, including the giver, the recipient, *and* anyone else who witnesses the deed. This means that if an employee is aligned with an organization's mission, any progress the organization makes *feels* good to everyone within the system.

- **Don't surround yourself with "yes" people.** The people in an organization must feel empowered to push back against an entrepreneur who is experiencing destabilizing optimism, without facing retribution. That not only means you have to get the right people around you but it also means you can't be a bully. If your team is afraid to tell you no, that's a problem that will permeate every level of the organization. This means that the entire culture needs to change. Great leaders create a culture in which people aren't afraid to voice their opinions.

Chapter Seven

ESOP's Fable

"The best way to elevate yourself and your company is to elevate everybody in the process."

—Wendy Burton, World Tree

Once upon a time, an entrepreneur's dream came true. Her business was extremely successful. She employed hundreds of people who admired her and who enjoyed working for the company. When she first dreamed of the company 20 years before, this is exactly what she wanted.

One day, a representative from a private equity (PE) firm came to see her. He slid a folder across her desk. Inside was a proposition for buying a majority stake in the business. This deal would result in her putting 100 million dollars into her pocket. When she saw that number, she smiled.

So did the PE executive, and boy, did his teeth look sharp. She looked at the name on his business card: Brad Shinyteeth, MBA.

"How would this affect my employees?" she asked.

"However you want it to. I've seen very generous CEOs give each employee a bonus in these situations. Everyone is very happy to get a bonus," said Brad Shinyteeth.

The entrepreneur smiled at the thought. She loved her employees. Whenever she'd thought about selling the business, the number one thing that stopped her was wanting to do right by her employees.

Brad said, "Think of all you could do. You've earned this."

She couldn't help but agree. She had worked incredibly hard to get the company to this place. She was proud of everything she'd accomplished. But she'd be lying if she said she wasn't ready for the next adventure. And here was an opportunity to get a handsome payout, give each employee a generous bonus for their contributions, and get to turn her attention to her next endeavor. She told Brad Shinyteeth that she'd think it over.

That night she had a dream that she came into the office to find all of her employees packing their desks into cardboard boxes.

"What's going on?" she asked her COO, who had been with her since the beginning.

Through tears, the COO explained that half of the team was let go, and the other half was quitting. They didn't want to be led by this private equity company who treated them as if they were disposable.

"But I gave everyone a bonus!" the entrepreneur said. "Did that matter?"

"Sure," said the COO, "I think I'll live off of it while I look for my next job . . . if I can even find one at my age."

"I'm so sorry!" the entrepreneur said. "I tried to take care of you!"

A short bald man appeared at her side. "Who are you?" she asked.

"I'm Aesop," the man said.

"Like . . . Aesop's Fables?"

"That's the one," he said. "And I want to tell you a quick story. It's one of my own. It's called 'The Horse and Groom.' In this fable, a groom lovingly brushes a horse for hours, hoping to make the horse beautiful and happy. Yet the groom turns around and steals the horse's oats to sell. The horse reprimands him, saying, 'If you really wish me to be in good condition, you should groom me less and feed me more.' Do you know what the moral of this fable is?"

The entrepreneur looked around the office and saw nothing but empty, desolate workstations. "What is it?"

Aesop said, "The moral is: if you wish to do a service, do it right."

The entrepreneur said, "If I wish to do right by my employees, I need to ensure their future with the company, not give them a one-time bonus."

Aesop winked. "Exactly. I'm so happy my stories are still relevant. Now, let me tell you about another fable. It's ESOP's fable. In this story, an entrepreneur is approached by a greedy private equity firm that wants to buy the majority stake of her business. She looks at the offer and realizes how valuable her company is, but that it's even more valuable if the people who have put years of their lives into its success are also owners. So, instead of taking the firm up on their offer, she sets up an ESOP. In turn, she extracts some cash from her business while continuing to participate in its growth and gives ownership to those amazing people who helped her to get to this level of success. In the future, if she does decide to sell to an outside party, she has ensured that everybody wins. Even the lowest-paid employee becomes a millionaire."

The entrepreneur listened to Aesop's story. She was torn. She didn't want this nightmarish future for her company, but she also wanted to reap her rewards now rather than later.

Aesop seemed to understand her dilemma. "Remember, without the horse, the groom has no job. Only a fool believes that they've created their success individually when it's a team that makes it happen."

This was exactly what the entrepreneur needed to hear. She turned down Brad Shinyteeth and set up an ESOP (employee stock ownership plan) for her employees, which resulted in her being able to extract a big sum of money from the company to seed her next idea. Two years later, she sold the majority of her company in a deal that was four times larger than the original offer. Her employees had ownership in the company and went on to work there for many years to come. When they retired, even the lowest-paid employee owned millions of dollars in company stock.

ESOP: the Celebration of all Celebrations

For *Entrepreneurland*, I've focused more on the benefits of ESOPs than the ins-and-outs of how they work. If you'd like a deeper look into ESOPs, I interviewed the ESOP expert, Richard Harmon, for Chapter 15 of *Pitchology*. You can hear that interview on the

Pitchology podcast episode, "ESOPs with Richard Harmon," available on all podcast platforms.

- **A PE firm could be the worst type of investor to align with.** Think about it. They're going to do anything and everything they can to make their money back. Often, they will dismantle a company for its parts and dump the people to the side if that means they can make their money back more quickly. This isn't *always* the case, but in my experience, entrepreneurs are biologically allergic to PE firms and their ways. More often than not, the entrepreneur leaves piles of money on the table as a result of an abandoned employment contract with milestones.

- **Share the wealth.** An ESOP allows an entrepreneur to get paid, save a ton in taxes, share equity with the people who helped grow the company, and often remain in control to continue to build the business. There's nothing more generous than an entrepreneur who wants to consider the ESOP structure in order to reward and recognize the people who have helped them have great success.

- **There's not *only* one way to exit, or extract cash from, your business.** Many people sell their companies to the wrong party because they don't know the many ways to sell or simply get paid for their business. It's not a matter of *if* but *when* you want to extract cash from your company and go enjoy your life. An ESOP is an excellent way to be able to exit *and* continue to be involved in the growth of the company, but it's not an overnight solution. The best time to start an ESOP is usually years in advance and when your company is very profitable.

- **Beware the psychological "check out."** Often, when an entrepreneur is approached by a PE firm or any other potential acquirer, they get so wrapped up in dreaming about the future without their company that they check out psychologically. This puts the entrepreneur at a huge disadvantage, especially when negotiating with a PE firm. The best thing to do is know your options *before* engaging with Brad Shinyteeth. But if you find yourself in this situation, try not to check out so completely that you lose sight of your options. This is exactly why I wrote *Pitchology*: to share many options.

Aesop isn't going to show up with any wisdom, but your closest team members or mentors, or both, might.

- **"Cream off the top" a.k.a. don't gouge your business.** Take your financial perks when things are good, and a little bit at a time. A lot of people don't know how to effectively extract cash from their company without putting themselves in financial danger or ruin. There have been a few times where I gouged my company because it was the only place I had money and I had to take it out. Later, I realized I had shortchanged myself by taking too much. You can't always anticipate a downturn or the obligation to fund extraordinary events such as employee errors, lawsuits, uninsured loss of property, or anything not in your ordinarily anticipated expenses. An ESOP is one way to extract cash from your company *and* minimize your tax burden too.

Chapter Eight

Who Hunter

> *"Our eyes can only see and our ears only hear what our brain is looking for."*

—Dan Sullivan

B.B. Wolf's security company was by far his best venture, but the journey wasn't seamless. Before he became the founder and CEO of the multi-million-dollar B.B. Wolf Enterprises, he had to learn a few lessons the hard way. One of those lessons was how important it is to get the right people in the right seats.

B.B. first got into the security business because rats were invading his hometown of Pigville, which, as you may have guessed, was primarily made up of pig residents. Pigville's economy revolved around corn and grain production. Rats were the biggest threat to Pigville's economy as they ate through stores of grain in the silos, which left many a farmer in a precarious financial situation. Even those pigs who weren't farmers feared the rats, since many Pigville residents lived in houses made of straw and wood. The rats chewed through the foundations, causing the pigs thousands of dollars in home repairs.

B.B. saw a way to start a company that made Pigville a better place to live, so he started B.B. Wolf Security Systems. In the beginning, B.B. patrolled alone. He charged the farmers a fee and spent his nights traveling from farm to farm, chasing off rats as he saw them. He quickly realized he couldn't run the business and perform all the labor himself. He needed to hire.

One day he saw a cat stalking a rat. He was impressed with the cat's agility and speed. He and the cat struck up a conversation and found out that they had a lot in common. They were both smart, skilled hunters, and they both had excellent night vision.

B.B. saw an opportunity to cover more ground and make his business more effective. He hired three cats to patrol different areas of Pigville. The first week was amazing. The cats were naturals. They didn't require any micromanaging from B.B. The weekly report from that first week showed enormous growth in the number of rats both chased and killed. Several other farmers signed up for B.B.'s security services. B.B. couldn't believe his luck.

But soon the problems started. The independence B.B. loved about the cats soon proved itself to be an issue. The cats were independent to the point that they couldn't take instruction from B.B. at all. B.B. had to admit the cats were excellent hunters, but they didn't stay focused on the rats. They chased birds, lizards, moles, and occasionally got distracted by inanimate objects like ribbons. B.B. tried to call an all-paws-on-deck meeting to discuss this, but only one cat showed up, and even he was late.

A few weeks later, a new problem emerged. B.B. couldn't spend one hour alone without a cat popping in, jumping onto his desk, and, while licking its butt with its hind leg in the air, telling B.B. about some exciting new idea of what else the company could do.

The hardest part for B.B. was that some of these ideas were good. He also loved looking out at the horizon and dreaming about the future. But his business was new and there simply wasn't enough time to devote to dreaming. They needed to show signs of steady and reliable growth before they could afford to gaze at the horizon.

B.B. started to worry that the cats weren't going to be the amazing rat-hunting machines he needed. They had the skills and the natural ability, but there was something not quite right about his workforce.

One night, B.B. was walking home from work late when he spotted a rat trying to sneak into a grain silo. He crouched low, expecting one of his team of cats to pounce any second. Instead, from behind the silo, he heard some terrible screeching. The rat heard the screeching too and ran for cover.

B.B. went to investigate behind the silo, where he found two of his cat employees in a face-off, backs arched, tails fluffed. B.B. broke up the fight.

"While you two were fighting over who-knows-what, a rat just got away!" B.B. growled.

The cats hissed and ran off.

B.B. sat down and mulled over what had just happened. Those cats are on their last chance, he thought. He heard some scratching from the silo. The rat was back.

B.B. inched toward the rat. He was seconds away from pouncing when all of a sudden an owl snatched up the rat right in front of B.B.

He watched, astounded, as the owl sailed silently up into the treetops.

He heard a gentle laugh from a nearby tree. Another owl was perched on a low branch, watching him.

"Why are you laughing?" B.B. practically growled.

"Cats, amiright?" the owl responded.

The hairs on B.B.'s back softened.

"I'm Dean," said the owl.

"I'm B.B.," said B.B. "And I'm about to go fire some cats and go back to working alone."

Dean blinked his huge eyes. "At some point, a cow has to find someone else to milk her. Working alone doesn't work well as soon as you start to grow your business."

B.B. sighed. "What am I supposed to do with these cats, then? You know, the hardest part for me is that even though I'm disappointed in them, everything they're doing is something I would do or have done. We're too much alike to work together."

"At the risk of being a stereotypical owl, I do have some words of wisdom for you."

"Please, go ahead," said B.B.

"If you hire in your likeness, you'll get a lot of 'yous' trying to run the show. If you need a job performed, you don't need another you. You need a Hoo-Hoooo!"

"A what?"

"A Who[1]. A Who[1] is someone whose unique abilities[1] are a total complement to a certain role. Often the most necessary Who[1] holds a skillset that you don't."

B.B. considered this. "Cats aren't the only animals who hunt rats."

"Indeed," said Dean. "When considering the unique skill sets of your Who[1], you may discover that it's not only what they can do but the manner in which they do it that makes them a Who[1] and not a you."

"The cats are already trying to run the business. That's what I want to do. I need someone to patrol at night and be reliable rat control. Do you think there are any owls who would like to come work for me?" said B.B.

Dean clacked his beak. "Owls?"

"Yes, I just saw an owl swoop silently out of nowhere and take a rat out. Plus, you can turn your head almost all the way around, and you can fly! That's an excellent skill for a security officer."

Dean seemed a little bashful. "Well, sure, but that's not . . ."

B.B. interrupted, "It's extremely unique. The cats are basically smaller wolves. But you . . . you have all these skills that we don't."

"Are you offering me a job?" Dean asked.

"Yes," said B.B, "but not just any job. I'm offering to pay you for the thing you do best. You can hunt rodents at night and get paid for it."

The next day, B.B. called a conference with his team of cats and told them it wasn't working out. The cats weren't upset. In fact, many of them had already started their own businesses. B.B.'s intuition told him that these cats' businesses weren't going to do very well, but he couldn't quite say why.

B.B. brought in a team of owls, and everything ran smoothly. He didn't know why he hadn't thought of owls to begin with. They were perfect for the job: naturally awake all night, silent hunters with unparalleled focus, and most obviously—they could fly! The owls proved to be smart and self-sufficient without encroaching on his leadership. The owls were the perfect fit because they shared the GRITT values (gratitude, respect, innovation, teamwork, and trustworthiness) that B.B. held so *dearly. Once B.B. got a taste for working with owls as his patrol team, he knew he'd never make the mistake of not having the right Who[1] for a task.*

B.B. was happy, his customers were happy, and the owls were happy. The only unhappy party was the rats.

With his team of Whos[1] in place, B.B. could set his sights on the future of his company, which included looking to the horizon to dream bigger.

The Difference Between Cats and Owls

Dean Jackson coined the phrase "Who, not how," which you might recognize as the title of a well-known entrepreneurial book. Well, Dean's friend and Strategic Coach founder, Dan Sullivan, resonated with the idea so hard that he and Dr. Benjamin Hardy wrote a book about it. (*Who, Not How[1]* by Dan Sullivan and Dr. Benjamin Hardy is dedicated to Dean.)

For Dean, the idea is more of a concept by which to live his life. I had the pleasure of interviewing Dean Jackson for this book. Scan the QR code to hear our entire conversation, in which we discuss unique ability[1], abundance mentality, and the power of sticking with a community for the long run. He also breaks down the concept of a Who[1]. The gist is this: we don't have to know how to do everything; we just have to know how to identify the people who have the unique abilities[1] to do it. Dean has some especially fun ways of illustrating this.

- **No one can do it alone**. A Who[1] Hunter is always on the lookout for someone whose unique skill set matches what is missing in the organization. You're always looking for the person who was literally put on earth to do what you need them to do.

- **Often people don't know their own unique abilities[1].** In our conversation, Dean makes the analogy of a bunch of cows who are trying to milk themselves, pasteurize the milk, bottle it, send it to market, and clean up afterward—before they realize that producing milk is *their* unique ability[1]. Once they realize this, they find a team who can handle the other stuff so the cows can just produce the milk. While a unique ability[1] is certainly something special about an individual, it is often an attribute they come by so naturally that they don't even notice it. Sometimes, the best way to find your unique abilities[1] is to ask other people what they rely on you for. There are exercises to help you find your unique abilities[1] in *Who, Not How.*

- **Fast track to done.** Dean explains how entrepreneurs usually excel at adaptive challenges where the answer is not known. We can figure it out or invent a solution, but we often get caught up in the technicalities of it, or in trying to teach other people how to do it. He says that once an entrepreneur has a solution to a problem, they come to a fork in the road. On one path, the entrepreneur will have to spend time learning "how" to navigate the technicalities or technology of the solution, probably learning by trial and error. This can be frustrating and slow. The other path is bringing in Whos[1] who possess the unique ability[1] to solve the issue at hand, or who can intuitively provide solutions. This is the fast track to done.

- **Whos[1] are not always entrepreneurial, but they can be.** In this story, the Whos[1] are owls who bring their unique abilities[1] to the role of rat patrollers. They are the perfect Whos[1] because they do the role so naturally, they've never even thought of it as a skill. However, in the Columbus story, Christopher Columbus is both the entrepreneur *and* the Who[1]. Columbus was both solving a problem for Spain and also had the entrepreneurial drive to be the innovator of the opportunity.

- **A business owner and an entrepreneur are not the same thing.** An entrepreneur is usually a business owner, but a business owner is not always an entrepreneur. In *The E-Myth Revisited,* Michael Gerber says that most people who start businesses are usually technicians suffering an entrepreneurial seizure, like a carpenter opening a contractor business or a poodle clipper opening a poodle clipping shop. But being able to execute the technical part of the business and creating a business are not the same thing. Gerber's mantra is "work on it, not in it." If the business needs you to be able to operate, then you have a job, not a business.

- **Just because a cat and an owl can both kill a rat doesn't mean they're equally suited for the job.** What constitutes a Who[1] is much more comprehensive than their unique ability[1] alone. You have to look into their history, their track record, their personality, the gut feeling you have about them, what other people are saying about them, etc. and draw a full picture before determining whether they're your Who.[1] B.B. Wolf wasn't terribly wrong when he hired the cats. There was a reason it seemed like a good idea. But soon enough, the lack of cultural alignment was undeniable. The cats didn't have a true passion to protect the community. They were more interested in figuring out how they could further capitalize on the situation than being part of a team.

- **You often learn more about your values when things *don't* go right.** The values I hold the most dearly are GRITT: gratitude, respect, innovation, teamwork, and trustworthiness. I was able to identify these not because of my idealism but through a series of relationships that didn't work. Often it's easier to identify your values when things go tragically wrong and then reverse engineer them!

Chapter Nine

Mesmerized By Our Own Ideas

"The best thing about entrepreneurs is their optimism. The worst thing about entrepreneurs is their optimism!"

—Jack Welch

Franz Mesmer was a German physicist whose theories had great influence on the development of modern-day hypnosis. Even if you think you've never heard of him, you most certainly have. His last name serves as the root of the word "mesmerize."

Franz was a talented young man with many ideas. He believed that blockages to the "animal magnetism" that flows through the body created illnesses, and that by rebalancing the magnetism (through modern-day hypnotism), he could heal people.

His desire to heal many came from watching his sister deal with debilitating melancholia (what we call depression today) during her teenage years and young adulthood that was often so severe she could not leave her bed for days. She was his willing test subject while he adapted his technique. He sat in front of her in their salon and gently swung a gold pocket watch in front of her eyes, reciting certain ideas or commands to move the animal magnetism through her blockages.

After a few months, his sister's melancholia waned, and she started finding joy in everyday pleasures again. On Christmas day, 1754, his sister arrived in the salon with hand-embroidered handkerchiefs for each member of the family; embroidery had been a hobby she once loved but gave up at the height of her melancholia. She declared herself healed and threw her arms around Franz. "You saved me," she said.

Following his sister's transformation, Franz successfully moved the animal magnetism in a few more townspeople, following the same procedure in the salon in his family home.

Franz wanted to show the world his system of healing others. He knew he possessed a special talent. He decided to embark on a tour of Europe during which he would heal people as a form of spectacle. He could sell tickets and perhaps merchandise, but he would need to find an investor to fund his venture.

Franz and his family approached a wealthy man, Herr Müller, to ask him for funds for the new expansion.

Müller thought about the proposition. He had heard talk from other townspeople whom Franz had healed. And here was Fraulein Mesmer, rosy-cheeked and a glint of joy in her eye after having been bedridden by melancholia for months. Müller thought this endeavor was a good one. However, he was less interested in funding the trip than he was in investing in the intellectual property. He instructed Franz to write a manual, therefore becoming the proprietor of his own invention. To write the manual, Franz would have to recreate the healing in new places and with other people. He must be sure of his process and its effectiveness before he could reliably sell it. Otherwise, people would call him a fraud. But if he created a manual, he could then lead classes to teach others how to harness the animal magnetism, and those people could teach others, and so on, thereby making Franz and his family very wealthy. Müller offered Franz a sum of money to sustain him as he conducted research and wrote the manual and told Franz that once the manual was completed, Franz could approach him again about the trip.

Franz's parents believed in Franz's abilities so thoroughly that they were willing to use the deed to their family home as collateral against Herr Müller's loan.

Franz agreed to the terms of the investment and received the money, but on the way home, he expressed disdain to his family. "If I write a manual and do the required research, it will take me more than a year, and even longer to have it pressed! If I were just to go on my tour, just me and my pocket watch, I could leave in the spring."

"Franz, don't be hasty," his father said. "Don't you think Herr Müller knows more than you do about investments and business?"

Franz was infuriated at this suggestion. "He may know about business, but he doesn't know anything about my skills and talents. His idea will do nothing but hold me back!" he cried. With that, he stopped talking and refused to discuss his plans with his family again.

Franz decided he couldn't wait. Herr Müller would see. Franz would go around the region and heal so many people that his name would become synonymous with miracles.

Franz left in March without telling Herr Müller. His family didn't know his plans to leave until the morning he arrived downstairs with his steamer trunk packed. They knew they could do nothing to dissuade him, but prayed that he would have success.

On his first stop in Vienna, he learned that his healing appointment was going to be a public spectacle. In the town square in front of a crowd of spectators, Franz was to heal a nobleman's wife who had been stricken with a sudden and complete case of mutism. He swung the pocket watch. He murmured his commands.

And nothing happened.

He assured the crowd that his work often took multiple sessions. He tossed and turned all night, fretful that the next day's session would also be a failure.

The next session failed as well. As did the next. He left Vienna defeated. His reputation had already preceded him in Salzburg, where he was to heal a young man who suffered from narcolepsy after having fallen off a horse.

Again, the session only resulted in a disappointed crowd and a humiliated Franz—no movement of animal magnetism.

Embarrassed and dejected, Franz returned to Germany. He had spent almost all of Herr Müller's investment on lodging in Vienna and Salzburg. Neither patient's family was willing to pay him for his failed attempts. He was almost penniless.

The day after Franz arrived home, Herr Müller came to visit. Franz sheepishly met him in the salon.

Herr Müller said, "I hear you decided to go public with your roadshow and failed. I assume you didn't do your research? Did you not write the manual we agreed upon?"

"I didn't write it," Franz said.

"So I've heard," Herr Müller said. "Well, it seems as though I should ask for the return of my investment, then, since you did not deliver its terms."

Franz couldn't believe he had lost his family home. In a fit of rage, Franz stood up, took the watch out of his pocket, and hurled it against the mirror behind Herr Müller. "You would kick my family out onto the street? What kind of person are you, anyway?"

Herr Müller looked at the shattered mirror. "No, Franz, I will not kick your family out onto the street. This is your lesson to learn, not theirs. I will not take their home, as that is not my nature, but I will hold you personally liable for the note." Herr Müller picked up the pocket watch and said "I will take this as collateral." He knew an impossible young man when he saw one. The truth was that once, long ago, Herr Müller himself was a lot like Franz. He, too, had had to confront his ego the hard way.

Alone in the salon, Franz looked at his reflection in the shards of mirror. Behind him was the chair where his patients had sat when he had so successfully moved their animal magnetism. The light from the window danced across the room, refracted in new and unexpected ways in the broken glass.

He called for his sister to come to the salon. "Herr Müller took my pocket watch! I'll never be able to move animal magnetism without it!" he cried.

His sister said, "I think anything reflective or shiny would work. There was always a glint of light from the pocket watch that moved across my eyes just so, and that always made me feel sleepy."

Franz rushed to the kitchen and returned with a large metal spoon. His sister sat how she always had, between the mirror and the window. Franz waved the spoon back and forth.

"The light is different," she said, turning to look at the mirror. "The mirror isn't reflecting it how it used to, now that it's broken."

Now the light refracted prismatically and uncontrollably. Franz sank down to his knees. The most important ingredient had been the light from the mirror reflected in the pocket watch.

"If we had performed the tests to write the manual as Herr Müller suggested, we would've figured that out," his sister said.

"I know that," said Franz. He felt deeply ashamed at his arrogance. He had been so entranced by his own idea and talent that he'd scoffed at his investor's advice and ruined his opportunity for greatness.

To this day, young inventors and entrepreneurs are sometimes so mesmerized by their own ideas that they fail to do their research to confirm their conclusions and thereby cause their own failure.

Entrepreneurial Investment Expectations: the Art of Using OPM Intentionally

- **Confidence will take you far. Narcissism won't.** Many entrepreneurs have been called narcissists. Some probably deserve that classification. Others might fit better under the "self-mesmerized" category. Either way, it will serve you well to confront your ego early and often by being open to coaching, as well as to others' insights and comments. As Ken Blanchard says, "None of us is as smart as all of us."

- **If you're an E looking for an EI, it is best to be coachable.** There is an alternative version of the Franz Mesmer story in which Franz admits his mistake and humbly asks Herr Müller to forgive him and help him proceed. Instead, Franz throws a tantrum, shattering not only a mirror, but Herr Müller's respect for him. Nobody wants to invest in a petulant child.

- **Don't believe your own bullshit, and don't expect an EI to, either.** It's *great* to have an idea you believe in, but overconfidence is detrimental. Of course, you want to have confidence as you pitch your idea to investors. However, don't get cocky and think you can pull one over on a potential EI by including bullshit projections on your presentation decks. Trust me—we know the difference. There is power and credibility in vulnerability.

- **Follow-up and accountability from the E is everything.** The MOU is very important, but follow-up and communication is more important. Although Herr Müller was clear on their mutual understanding, he failed to monitor and hold Franz accountable for the creation of the workbook. The MOU is good, but you need to have accountability, regular meetings, and communication.

- **Optimism needs to be supported by wisdom.** Getting to the Life's Work part of your journey feels amazing. But it's hard, if not impossible, to get there if you're spinning out on optimism when there isn't enough wisdom to support it. That's where an EI can make a huge difference in your journey, and I don't just mean by supplying capital. They can help you navigate the external *and* internal circumstances that can put your Life's Work in jeopardy. Most EIs are attracted to Es that remind them of themselves . . . ego and all.

- **Have something real.** In my conversation with Doug Brackmann back in Chapter Six, I asked him what he looks for in a potential E to invest in. He answered,

"Humility is the number one thing I look for before I throw money at anybody. I get to know him. I don't buy the narcissistic fantasy that [entrepreneurs] can paint: 'Oh my God, it's going to be so great!' Oh yeah, but what is it *now?* Before I invest, I want to know when it will become real."

Chapter Ten

Three Littlepigs & B.B. Wolf

> *"In business, I believe that if you focus only on the journey, you'll miss the whole adventure. Mergers and acquisitions are the adventure that teaches you the most."*

— Steve Distante

There once were three Littlepig siblings who lived in side-by-side houses in Pigville.

The oldest sibling was Marcus Littlepig. He had worked for a home-health aide business for 25 years. He was the second-in-command in the business, but now, he

looked around and realized he had grown with the company as far as he could. Marcus found himself in a difficult situation: if he ever wanted to make more money or have something more to aspire to at work, that meant finding another job. He would prefer to stay in the industry where he'd built his expertise, but that would mean moving out of Pigville and leaving his brother and sister. So Marcus resigned to remaining dissatisfied in his career for the foreseeable future.

The middle sibling was Jorge Littlepig. He worked for an insurance business. Like his brother, he was second-in-command. The future was looking grim for Jorge because the owner of the insurance business was in his 70s and wanted to retire but had no exit strategy. The only options were for the company to close—in which case Jorge and about 35 other pigs would lose their jobs—or for Jorge to step up and buy the company, but he didn't have the money to do that.

The youngest sibling was Lisa Littlepig. Like her brothers, she had also risen to be second-in-command at a business. She worked for B.B. Wolf Security, a nationwide business headquartered in the owner's hometown of Pigville. She'd had an excellent experience working for B.B. Wolf, even though her brothers cautioned her against taking the job.

You see, pigs had been taught to fear wolves. Wolves were notorious not only in Pigville but all over the country. They were known to be hungry and stop at nothing to make their businesses succeed, even if that meant exploiting pigs in the process.

Lisa Littlepig hated that stereotype about wolves. She had a great experience with B.B. She knew that even though B.B. was hungry for a successful business, he was motivated by wanting to see the world become a better and safer place. Since he had started his security business, the rat population in Pigville had plummeted, saving farmers from losing their stores of corn and grain. Lisa couldn't understand why residents of Pigville resented B.B. for his success. His success was contingent upon the safety of Pigville. That seemed like a good thing to Lisa.

So, when Lisa's brothers were in a predicament regarding the futures of the companies they worked for, Lisa suggested they talk to B.B. She wasn't surprised when Jorge snorted, "Are you serious? Do you have any idea what you're suggesting?"

Marcus was similarly aghast: "It's bad enough you work for that bloodthirsty canine. What could he possibly do for us? Put us out of our misery by eating us?"

This was the response Lisa had expected from her brothers. That's why the following Sunday, when the family had their regular bunch at Jorge's brick house, Lisa invited a special guest.

Knock knock knock.

"Who's there?" grunted Jorge.

"I'll get it!" said Lisa. She returned to the dining room with B.B.

Marcus squealed and fled the room. Jorge stayed at the table, but the color drained from his face.

"Jorge, this is B.B. Wolf. I want you to speak with him about your boss's exit strategy. Or, I guess I mean, lack of an exit strategy. Because I think there's a great third option you aren't considering," Lisa said.

Jorge's hooves were trembling under the table, but he told B.B. about his career, his role in the business, and the current predicament: his boss wanted to retire, but the right systems weren't in place for Jorge to become the company's new owner. Even if Jorge had the capital, it felt like a risky investment to make alone.

B.B. listened with interest. When Jorge was done, B.B. leaned forward with his paws crossed on the table. "Jorge, I see that you're a valuable member of this business. You could run it with your hooves tied behind your back—"

Jorge squealed in protest.

"Sorry, I shouldn't have said that. I mean you're a highly functioning 'Who¹' within this business. You're an incredible asset, and the business needs you so it can continue on. I think Lisa is right, here. There is a third solution, and it could be a win-win. All you need is the security in this transition to make sure you stay afloat."

"What do you suggest?" Jorge asked.

B.B. said, "I would love to negotiate B.B. Wolf Security acquiring your business, with you at the helm. Everyone in the system who wants to continue with the company will have the opportunity to do so, and seamlessly. Your boss can make a good chunk of money for his retirement. And I'll achieve a goal of diversifying my business. Lisa knows I've been searching for an opportunity just like this."

Jorge was understandably skeptical. "How do I know it'll happen just like that and you won't change your mind?"

B.B. smiled, but his sharp teeth didn't look threatening to Jorge. "Well, that's what contracts are for."

Jorge nodded, a little embarrassed that he'd asked that. "I'll talk to the owner," he said.

"Good," B.B. said.

Marcus Littlepig was listening from around the corner. He poked his head into the dining room and said, "So sorry, I had to take a call out here."

"Come in, Marcus," said B.B. "Tell me what's going on with your business."

Marcus told B.B. how the home-health aide company where he worked had completely stagnated. He was frustrated because the owners wanted to grow, but they didn't know what to do. They'd been talking about it for years, but nothing had changed. Marcus was uninspired and bored at work. He was unsure if he could find more opportunities without leaving Pigville. He valued living close to his family. In a perfect world, his company would grow and scale, and he could take on more responsibility and a bigger salary.

"I don't think the owners want out, though. They wouldn't just let you buy the company," Marcus said, a small edge to his tone.

B.B. considered what Marcus was saying. "No, this is not an acquisition. Just like your brother, you are an invaluable asset to this company. Losing you would be a major hit for them. But how can they expect you to spend the next 20 years of your life in the exact same role you're currently in? There is opportunity for growth and scaling, though, if the owners would consider a merger."

"What would that entail?" Marcus asked.

"You're dealing with talent, meaning your team is your product. You already know how to manage your team. You know how to mitigate risk in your industry. The only thing that's wrong here is that the owners haven't had an exponential mindset. Perhaps they need to develop their 'inner wolf.' That's what I can bring in. That, and security."

Marcus thought about it. "I'll talk to the owners," he said. "Thanks, B.B. I'm sorry I was so skeptical."

Both Littlepig brothers set up meetings between B.B. and the owners of their companies. B.B. acquired the insurance company and merged with the home-health aide company. Under B.B.'s mentorship, the Littlepig brothers still ran their businesses, but with much less liability and more security. B.B. was wise enough to know that culture is leadership-driven. It trickles down through organizations. After a merger or acquisition, sometimes employees leave because they're frustrated or disenchanted. But B.B. kept the existing leadership in place. He did everything he could to not rock the boat, and in turn, all of the employees stayed with the companies.

Lisa's contribution wasn't lost on B.B. He promoted Lisa to the head of the new M&A division of B.B. Wolf Enterprises. Her talent for recognizing opportunity was an incredible asset to B.B. Wolf Enterprises, which became a $500 million corporation within five years.

B.B.'s new mantra became: "I'll merge, and I'll acquire, and we'll all stay in business!"

And that's how the thing that Jorge and Marcus had always taken as a threat actually ended up being the biggest opportunity of their lives. B.B. Wolf's confidence, clarity, and aptitude for risk guided the pigs into partnering and collaborating. They were able to escape their dead-end employment and become the business owners they'd always dreamed of being. B.B.'s mentorship brought out their inner wolves. An important part of bringing out an inner wolf is sharing vulnerability with the pack.

When Jorge and Marcus eventually married and had children, some of the children were born with surprisingly sharp teeth and a layer of dark gray fur. It was well known in Pigville that wolves were wolves from birth, no matter who their parents were. While some parents didn't know what to do with wolves, Jorge and Marcus were thrilled to get to mentor their pups.

Everyone lived happily ever after.

"I'll Merge and I'll Acquire, and We'll All Stay in Business!"

I sat down with my friend and fellow wolf, AJ Caro, a lifelong serial entrepreneur who truly embodies the benefits of M&A. His strategic acquisitions of a home-health aide business and an insurance company served as the inspiration for the Littlepigs story above. Scan the QR code to access my full conversation with AJ, where we take a deep dive into M&A.

- **Diversification is important.** Diversification across different industries should bring longer-term stability, as one economic event would not be destabilizing enough to tank any of your businesses.

- **Diversification allows for a variety of activities.** Entrepreneurs tend to bore easily, so having a lot of different activities can offer longevity in more ways than just buffering for a market downturn.

- **Diversification has its cons too.** AJ explains in our interview that if your goal is to grow a very large company and then have an exit plan, then being diversified is not necessarily the best move. Diversification can take your concentrated growth efforts into multiple industries—which does create multiple streams of income—but not one larger company, which will likely hold higher value.

- **M&A can be a win-win.** Like Jorge Littlepig, who wasn't set up for success when his boss wanted to retire, a merger or acquisition can often help someone retire *and* retain many of the jobs for their team. Looking for companies in their sunset stage can help ensure a win-win. One of the greatest benefits to acquiring a "sunsetting" business is to acquire and mentor the "A players" from the company to manage and ultimately grow that new venture with minimal participation. Leaders are always on a mission to find great talent and identify their unique gifts.

- **Acquire strategically.** The best time to acquire a disaster relief company is before a tornado, hurricane, or earthquake hits, not after. This is generally true for a product or service that is opposite of a normal market. Acquiring a business like this for a reasonable price can pay off immensely in the event of a disaster, or whatever it takes to change the normal market. You can make headway in diversification through M&A, then develop those businesses under stable circumstances.

- **Savings is the first expense.** In the world of cycles, never gouge your business. Make saving your first expense. In a downturn market, that is the time to access your savings for an acquisition.

- **"Buy when there's blood in the streets, even if the blood is your own."** —Baron Rothschild (attributed). It is often advantageous to invest (or acquire) during a big market downturn or cataclysmic event. This is why saving for rainy days is always a good strategy whenever possible. Another strategy involves relationships. When you identify businesses that may be good M&A opportunities for you in a few years' time, keep an open line of communication with the current owners. If something happens and they decide to sell the business, they'll come to you as a lifeline.

Chapter Eleven

It's a Wonderful Drive

"The best way to predict the future is to invent it."

—Alan Kay

Elodie had never been happier to see her pillow, but once she settled her head on it, she knew she wouldn't be able to sleep. It had been, with no exaggeration, the worst day of her life. Her eyes were puffy from crying. Her head throbbed. Worst of all, she knew she had caused about 300 other people's Worst Day Ever in today's mass layoff. When she'd pursued her entrepreneurial dreams, this was not at all what she thought it would be like.

Elodie was the chairwoman of an electric car company called EleX. Before that, she'd had success as the CEO of a startup that had exploded into a worldwide phenomenon. She'd sold her shares of that company to fund EleX, but now that was looking like that was a mistake. The 2008 recession had been a major setback, and now, four years later, the company was still struggling to find its momentum. Elodie had already invested as much as she could into EleX. This time she'd had to lay off over half of her staff.

Her head still swirled with the sad, disappointed faces of the people she cared for deeply as, one by one, they'd left her office.

She turned on the TV to try to distract herself from her thoughts. But lo and behold if it wasn't Bob Putz, the head of the oil lobby, arrogantly smoking his cigar on the news. His television appearances were rare, but there he was, standing in front of the EleX headquarters, telling a reporter how unstable the electric car industry was and how the evil EleX had just laid off 300 workers. The last time she'd seen his face on TV was in 2010 when he was seeding rumors—based on one report from a faulty prototype—that EleX batteries spontaneously combusted. He followed that up with somehow getting the government to give tax credits to everyone who bought a gas-guzzling Bummer.

Elodie turned off the TV. She knew he was wrong. But she worried she didn't have the energy to put more years into this business. She couldn't imagine trying to drum up more capital from private investors, and she wasn't optimistic that she could secure any substantial loans after the layoffs. She was burned out and exhausted.

She did what she had to do to get to sleep: she took an Ambien. They sometimes gave her crazy dreams, but at least the dreams would be better than being awake on this terrible night.

As she was falling asleep, Elodie was once again ruminating on her squashed dreams of reducing carbon emissions. She had wanted to make the air safer to breathe for people who live near highways, especially highways that were built through poor neighborhoods, because the emissions often caused cancer in residents. She had wanted to break dependence on oil. She had wanted . . . she had wanted . . .

Beep Beep Beep

Was that her alarm clock? It was still dark out.

Swish Buzz Beep

Elodie opened her eyes a sliver, then sat bolt upright.

Iron Man was standing next to her bed. Elodie screamed.

Iron Man hurried to take off his intimidating helmet. "Don't be frightened, Elodie. It's me, Robert Downey Jr." Sure enough, Robert Downey Jr.'s handsome face was smiling at her from inside the tech suit.

"What are you doing here?" Elodie asked.

"I heard you were thinking of selling EleX, and I wanted to try to change your mind," he replied.

"My mind is made up," she said.

"Well, can I at least have the chance to try?"

She looked at Robert Downey Jr.'s big brown eyes and couldn't refuse.

"Great, let's go!" he said, putting his Iron Man helmet back on. He grabbed Elodie by the hand and led her outside to a model of EleX she'd never seen before.

"What car is this?" Elodie asked.

"It's one of your newest models," Iron Man said, "and it can fly."

He pressed the button and suddenly the car ascended straight up and—Zip—they were flying across the city.

Elodie was speechless. She looked down across the city, ready to marvel at its beauty like she always did from an airplane, but something was different. The lights were all dull and gray. It looked like they were flying through a cloud.

"Why is it so dark?" she said.

"It's smog," said Iron Man. "Every one of those cars clogging the interstate system is running on the last bits of oil that are left on the planet."

Iron Man navigated the car closer to the highway and rolled down the windows.

Elodie immediately choked. The air was so thick with exhaust fumes she couldn't inhale. The EleX's dashboard started flashing the warning: "Extremely Poor Air Quality Alert!"

"Roll it up! Roll it up!" Elodie said.

"How do you think they feel?" Iron Man pointed to the houses on either side of the interstate. "Their health has completely deteriorated."

"Is it like this everywhere?" Elodie asked.

"Well, not in Venice, New Orleans, and Miami. Those don't even exist anymore because the glaciers completely melted."

"Oh my God!"

"By the time people actually believed that we needed an alternative to oil, it was too late. Putz basically got his wish of there being two Bummers in every American garage. Of course, he died years ago and doesn't have to see the mess he caused. Now the world economy is on the brink of collapse. In a year's time, none of these internal combustion engines will be running, and the cars will just be discarded on the side of the road to rust."

"Let me guess: Bob Putz became the president, didn't he?" Elodie joked.

"Yes, he did."

"You're kidding, right?"

Iron Man's heart battery dimmed slightly. "I'm afraid I'm not."

Elodie was shaken by this grim picture of the future, but why was it her responsibility? Wasn't there someone else who cared as much as she did? Someone who hadn't tried and failed repeatedly? Why did the world's future depend on her alone?

Iron Man could feel her sinking into this train of thought. "Before you make up your mind, I have one more thing to show you," he said, and rolled down her window.

Elodie held her breath, but quickly realized she didn't need to. The smog was gone. Solar panels glinted in the twinkling lights of the city.

"Where are we?" she asked.

"Same spot, just with you in it," Iron Man said.

Elodie peered down at the interstate below. There were cars on it, but not quite so many. And they were almost silent. The cars emitted no sound other than the tires on the pavement. "It's so quiet," she said.

"It's actually pretty quiet everywhere now that nobody drives those noisy gas engines around."

"That's amazing," she said.

"And what do you smell?" Iron Man asked.

Elodie breathed deeply. "Nothing," she said.

"This is what the future will look like if you find a way to continue with EleX. And this is only one tiny part. Overall carbon emissions have plummeted worldwide. Rates of cancer are down. You've invested in high-speed trains connecting every major city in the United States, finally giving people travel options that don't involve fossil fuels. And you've sent a pilot colony to Mars."

Elodie gasped. She hadn't told anyone about that idea, not even her most trusted advisors.

"How did I know?" Iron Man chuckled.

"How do I know you're not just making this up?" Elodie asked.

Iron Man replied, "Well, let's go check on you."

"Me? I'm alive? What year is it?"

"It's 2096. And today is your 125th birthday," he said as the car streaked across the sky. Moments later, they landed on the street in front of a house. Elodie looked through the windows and saw an old woman sitting on a sofa. Beside her were three small children. Adults bustled around the house, carrying empty plates to the sink.

"Those are your great-great grandchildren," he said.

Elodie hadn't even started thinking about having a family. She didn't know if she wanted to bring children into the world as it was. Her eyes filled with tears. "Look at how loved she is—I mean, how loved I am."

"You made the world a better place for generations to come. Now that's love."

Someone brought the older Elodie a slice of cake with a single candle in it. The older Elodie smiled, closed her eyes, and blew it out.

Elodie opened her eyes in her bed. It was morning. She immediately looked around for Iron Man, but this was real life. She threw her covers aside and crossed the room to her window. She pulled up the blinds. There in the distance was the smokestack from a factory she'd grown to loathe. Down below her building, the four lane street was choked with cars.

She knew it had been a dream, but it wasn't just a dream. It was unfolding before her eyes every day. Elodie knew she wouldn't give up, not today at least. She would spend the next several months securing funding. She wanted to create that world for the people she loved as well as for the people she would never know.

But something else motivated Elodie other than pure altruism. When Elodie saw the old woman blow out the candle, Elodie knew she made a wish. What would a 125-year-old who had already changed the world have to wish for? Was there more in store for her still? Were there more changes she could make? Perhaps this wasn't a dead end at all, but simply a traffic jam. And Elodie would do everything it took, give everything she had, to be able to know what her 125-year-old self had to wish for.

Drive, Risk & Free Will:
The Entrepreneurial Triangle

The three sides of the Entrepreneurial Triangle are qualities present in every entrepreneur. The combination of Drive, Risk, and Free Will can create extraordinary or catastrophic results based on our choices.

Drive is the internal energy source that we *must* expend—for good, for bad, or for who-knows-what. No matter what outcome it leads to, this energy source is undeniable.

Risk is the endorphin-generating bonus that really gets us going. Much like drive, it's just a given that it's there, but the choice of how to apply it is up to us. The bigger the risk, the more energy that is created.

Free Will from an entrepreneurial perspective is the ability to do what we want to do, when we want to do it. To create the uncreated, to dream big without limits, and to make the impossible possible—on our terms.

The triangle is equilateral, meaning all the sides are of equal length. As an entrepreneur grows and matures, they'll likely experience times when one side is longer than the others, and they'll experience some sort of stress or pain due to this imbalance. Over time and experience, this triangle becomes closer and closer to equilateral, and the entrepreneur starts to experience the magic of being able to harness the benefits of these energies without getting dragged into the dangers of any one of them being out of balance.

How do we create such ideal conditions for the equilateral triangle?

- awareness

- collaborating with your team

- starting with the end in mind

As an example of starting with the end in mind, Elodie's primary goal was to stop people from suffering from cancer generated from vehicle exhaust; the rest of the story was just her journey to get there.

Driven to Your Greatness

Before writing this chapter, I sat down with my friend Salim Ismail, author of *Exponential Organizations*^ and the sequel *Exponential Organizations 2.0: The New Playbook for 10x Growth and Impact*^, to discuss the ins-and-outs of Entrepreneurial drive. Scan the QR code to access the entire conversation.

- **Your Life's Work may require money, but it's never *about* money.** It's bigger than that. It's usually something that is visceral, or at your core of being, that is a challenge or opportunity to have a massive impact on both you (the entrepreneur) and many others. In most cases, it becomes your legacy because it's so beneficial. As an example, my friend Joe Polish's Life's Work is the Genius Recovery Network*, a foundation that provides assistance and resources to people who are suffering with addiction.

- **For EIs, often the drive of the entrepreneur is more alluring than the company itself—we buy the drive, not the company.** In my interview with Salim, he tells me the story of his friend in Silicon Valley who has created seven venture-backed companies that have all failed—but company number eight became a billion-dollar company. Salim found out that the same venture capitalist (VC) firm funded this friend on attempts five, six, seven, and eight. Salim asked the people at the VC firm why they continued to back this guy even though he kept failing, and they said, "There's one thing we know about him, which is that he's completely crazy, and he's never going to stop. When he succeeds, we want to be there. And he's gonna succeed at some point because he's never going to stop."

- **Efficiency and predictability aren't enough anymore.** In our conversation, Salim explains how the old paradigm of a sustainable organization used to be based around efficiency and predictability. Now, he says that organizations need to be architected for agility, flexibility, adaptability, and speed in order to truly succeed in today's market. A perfect example of this is AI. If you're not paying attention to what's going on, you could become irrelevant overnight. This is a perfect position for the entrepreneur to continue to add value to their organization by keeping their eye on the future and developing a path forward. I personally belong to a few organizations, especially Abundance 360, where I learn about budding technologies in early stages and determine if they are relevant yet to my companies.

- **Evolve to wisdom.** Salim and I speak about the thrill of momentum we feel when we have a new idea, or even see a new avenue in the direction of our Life's Work.

I ask him, "Does anything stop you?"

He says, "Just some common sense every once in a while."

I reply, "That's wisdom."

In this context, I define wisdom as

- building immunity into your organization to ensure that it survives the waves of your creativity;

- being willing to recognize that your innovation has the potential to do more harm than good to the organization overall; and

- discerning which paths not to take.

- **Know your highest and best use for the organization.** Sometimes the CEO and president role isn't where the entrepreneur needs to be forever. I recently stepped down from the role of CEO and president and assumed the position of founder and chairman in my own company. I realized that I have a tendency to intentionally mess things up or piss people off, because I can(?), not because it's beneficial to the organization. I find that my role as visionary and coach for my C-suite is much healthier for the organization, and the day-to-day leaders are much better at harmony and consistency than I'd been.

- **Your ideal space may be at the edge.** There's a saying that goes, "If you're not living on the edge, you're taking up too much f#cking space." Salim discusses how the entrepreneur/founder may be happiest existing more at the edges of the company— where they can dabble with new ideas without being a destabilizing force—than at the helm. From that place, they can still create, influence, and drive the company.

- **Being an "arsonist" can give you the illusion of purpose.** I hear my fellow entrepreneurs say, "I'm constantly putting out fires!" My go-to response to this is, "Are you a paid firefighter, a volunteer firefighter, or an arsonist?" Their heads turn like a dog hearing a high-pitched noise. They know *exactly* what I mean. This is often a huge *"Aha!"* moment for people who realize that they long for the days when their business was a dependent baby who needed a hero. Now they're intentionally (or subconsciously) messing things up so they can have the opportunity to step in as the hero again. Learn to discern when you're just looking to blow shit up for the thrill of it.

- **Arson can be a reaction to metamorphosis.** It sounds counter-intuitive to think that this arson could be indicative of a good thing, but I've noticed a pattern in my fellow entrepreneurs. Often, when people start lighting their own fires to put out, it stems from the fact that the business has matured to a place where it is no longer dependent on the entrepreneur. Perhaps the right Whos[1] are in place and the company runs smoothly on its own. This can be a scary feeling for entrepreneurs, so they mess it up so they can find meaning. I encourage people in this space to replace their impulse to start the fire with an appreciation that their hard work has paid off.

- **Learn how to harness your drive in a beneficial way for everybody.** It doesn't matter how good your ideas are if you're constantly shifting the purpose of your organization. If you're repurposing your talent to new roles too often, no one will ever be able to master their position. This will lead to eye rolling and frustration from your team, or worse—A-players leaving the organization.

- **Consider creating an internal research and development team as an explorer.** To expand on the above point, you can create an R&D team that serves that explorative purpose without stressing out your existing business or pulling your nucleus team off their jobs. R&D goes out, brings back knowledge, and then as a team, you can decide whether a new idea is a viable part of your existing company, a new standalone company, or needs to be left on the shelf. Remember, being too early to an idea is just as dangerous as being too late. Sometimes things need to sit on the shelf for a while before they become truly viable.

- **The luge can be a good thing.** The thing about a luge is there's no getting off. To accomplish big projects, I need to have a "leave the world behind" mindset so I can focus intensely on the project at hand. This gives me permission to say "no" to any outside requests while I'm working on a big project. People respect that! Sometimes it's wise to create small, metaphorical luges for yourself to ensure that you see something through. When you're in a luge, you're accountable for results and deadlines. When you know how to harness the power of a luge, you can use it to create periods of commitment and intense focus so you can create BIG things. In writing this book, I assembled a team of Whos[1] and a series of deadlines that demanded my singular focus. This created a luge I couldn't help but ride straight from the idea to holding the book in my hands!

Chapter Twelve

AI, Crypto, Cannabis, and . . . Tulips?

> *"Those who cannot remember the past are condemned to repeat it."*
>
> **—George Santayana**

Let me tell you the cautionary tale of Tulipmania and a man who was swept away in its empty promises.

Willem Vosmeer was an ambitious man. He worked hard and saved diligently. He was born into a middle-class family in Amsterdam, but always dreamed of owning one of the grand houses along the main canal. The Dutch Golden Age ushered in the potential for prosperity unavailable to previous generations of middle-class Dutchmen. Willem grew up in a small, yet sturdy home, which his parents willed to him when they died. Willem's father had always wanted to live on the canal but never got the chance. Willem was determined that he would grow old in one of those houses and pass it along to his family so the Vosmeers would always have a place along the canal.

Willem worked for the Dutch East India Company, a global trading company. Occasionally, he saw local middle-class merchants get very wealthy through the deals Willem struck with traders abroad. Willem started wondering if he could do the same.

In 1633, Willem noticed a large influx of a particular item from the Ottoman Empire: tulip bulbs. Some of the wealthier residents of Amsterdam had been growing tulips for years. Tulips were quite the symbol of wealth. One of Willem's coworkers told Willem that his ledgers showed tulip bulbs were selling for outrageous sums. Maybe he and Willem should consider buying some tulip bulbs as well.

That's ridiculous, thought Willem. I don't even have a garden. What need do I have for a tulip bulb?

Willem didn't buy any bulbs, but his friend did. And a year later, his friend had made enough money to quit his job and move into his new four-story home on the canal.

Willem was distraught. If only he had bought the bulbs last year. Now some of the more prized species were selling for upwards of 2,000 florins! That was 10X his annual income, and far more than his life's savings. Two of those bulbs would buy the nicest house on the canal!

Meanwhile, tulips were becoming more and more popular. It seemed that even the more middle-class houses in Willem's neighborhood all had colorful gardens shooting up. Another of Willem's coworkers tripled his savings and was able to quit his job. When Willam asked that coworker, whom he didn't know to have over 2,000 florins of liquid cash sitting around, how he was able to fund the endeavor, the coworker smiled his snaggly grin. "I took out a loan, bought the bulbs during the dormant season, and then sold them at a profit before they flowered. I paid off the loans, and now I'm rich!"

"Isn't that risky?" asked Willem.

"No, listen to this: some of the bulbs are blooming in this fascinating and rare pattern, and those are fetching the highest dollar amounts and are in the highest demand. But you can't unearth a tulip while it's in bloom, so instead, while it's in bloom you can actually buy a contract to purchase it, knowing exactly what it looks like and its rarity and value. No surprises. Then during the dormant season, they dig it up and ship the bulb to you. Before it arrives, you sell the contract for an even higher price," said his coworker. "And you don't even have to dig around in the dirt."

It sounded too good to be true. Willem found out that there would be a wave of seven-year-old bulbs blooming in the following season. (Bulbs took seven to twelve years to create their first bloom, and were not worth as much until their color and features had been identified.) He decided to get to the point that he owned a future contract for one of the rarest bulbs.

There was a new territory entering the market: France, with their ridiculous powdered wigs and chateaux. He'd make a fortune selling these exquisitely rare bulbs to the French. At the end of the 1636 growing season, Willem made his move. He used his family home for leverage against a loan. Armed with a few hundred florins, he went to the tavern where people traded bulbs. He bought a contract for a run-of-the-mill bulb. The next week, he sold that contract for a profit and bought himself a slightly more expensive contract for a better bulb. He repeated this process several times, until eventually he owned a contract for a bulb that was worth almost the equivalent of 2,000 florins.

But that payout would never come. In February 1637, the prices of the coveted bulbs started plummeting. Willem rushed to sell his contract, but no one wanted to buy it. The future contracts were about as valuable as the paper they were printed on.

Tulip growers flocked to the city of Utrect to create an assembly that could enforce a legal basis for these contracts. After months of deliberation, the best they could come up with was a law that stated that all contracts entered into before

December of 1636 would be binding, while those that came later could be canceled for a fee equal to 10% of the contracted price.

Willem, along with hundreds of other tulip sellers, waited in excruciating anticipation while the Court of Holland deliberated. The issue toggled back and forth between different bureaucratic entities for the next three years, but in the end, most of the contracts were never honored.

Willem lost his life savings and worse, the family home full of the memories of his parents. Although he worked for the rest of his life, he was never able to buy that home on the canal.

As the years went by, the ordeal became known as "tulipmania," and people laughed at how ridiculous it was to spend so much money on tulip bulbs. But market bubbles would continue to come and go for centuries to come, and each time, the craze revolved around something that had the potential to be deemed frivolous just a few years later.

Greater Fool Theory

The Greater Fool Theory suggests that it's possible to make money even on goods with over-inflated prices as long as you can find someone else (the greater fool) to buy it for more. The Greater Fool Theory also implicates the original fool.

The point of studying past manias and market bubbles is *not* to gawk at the ridiculousness of whatever fad came and went. As impractical as tulips may seem to a modern person, imagine explaining to a 17th century Dutchman how much people spent on NFTs in 2021. (And good luck explaining exactly *what* an NFT is.) This goes for crypto, cannabis, AI, etc. Remember pet rocks?

Let me be clear: this is not advice to not participate *at all* with manias. Dabbling to a certain extent can be stimulating, even if it doesn't end up being lucrative. We have a huge desire for risk, and we also get pretty bad FOMO, so it's nice to scratch that itch. This advice is supposed to caution you not to get *swept away* in a mania, not to discourage you from participating in a way that won't result in you losing everything.

The point of studying past manias *is* to learn the signs of a mania, the expected trajectory, human psychology, and how you can leverage the opportunity while minimizing your exposure to risk.

- **Tulipmania exhibits a classic market-bubble trajectory:**

  - psychological biases that predict the continuously climbing value of a product,

  - subsequent inflation, and

  - people buying said product on credit,

  - with a few legendary, insightful investors being able to get out of the cycle before losing everything, while many people—you guessed it—lose everything.

- **Learn to recognize a mania.** This will help you remain lucid during the times when a few people are getting unfathomably rich off of [fill in the blank] and someone is offering you an "in."

- **Don't be fooled by crowd psychology.** We all know that humans are susceptible to peer pressure. Just because everyone else is doing it doesn't mean you have to.

- **Don't put all your money in one place.** Enough said.

- **Don't let your judgment be clouded.** Most entrepreneurs, when they are deciding whether or not to invest in someone's idea, rely on both their own gut instincts and insight from trusted individuals. However, due to the hype around manias, I've seen people lose their faculties in these situations. I've seen people invest major money into people they don't even like, and they don't seem to care that it could be the biggest scam in the world. The mania spills over and clouds their better judgment.

- **Putting too much energy into trying to stay ahead of the curve means you're unlikely to gain expertise in a certain area.** There's been a recent shift in entrepreneurs' mindsets. The best way I can describe it is: it seems like they all have FOMO. I see them changing industries rapidly, sometimes spanning multiple industries in a year, simply chasing the money. There is very little fulfillment in that. Lacking expertise makes you more likely to make a bad investment in a market bubble.

- **Ask for insight from trusted collaborators.** PIN provides screening for the types of opportunities that are allowed to be pitched, minimizing members' exposure to those who are trying to hype up market bubbles. Additionally, it provides a forum where people can ask others for insight into certain trends. The community aspect of the platform also provides insight into potential investments, which is another amazing buffer for FOMO or clouded judgment, or both.

- **Know the right time to act**. A mania will have you believing you need to jump on the craze *right now*, but the truth is, many too-early companies die—both on their own and with OPM (other people's money). To some, OPM might as well be opium. They get addicted to it. They seek risks with it. And often, entrepreneurs' taste for risk is satisfied by risking OPM instead of their own. When people are raising capital for something that's cutting edge, the likelihood of failure is enormous. That's not to say you should never invest in something cutting-edge, but due diligence is important.

- **A mania can make you a lot of money . . . if your timing is *perfect*.** But the risk far outweighs the potential reward in *most* circumstances. It's dangerous to be too early *or* too late, especially when dealing with a fast-evolving sector such as technology. Investing in an early-stage company that takes off is obviously a good investment. But you also have to have a strong exit plan in place to protect your ass(ets) and take some money off the table.

- **Think of participating in a mania as feeding your inner wolf. Do it sparingly and with an eye for safer options.** Don't get mesmerized by the most obvious (and riskiest) aspect of a mania. Instead, leverage the opportunities. There's an old saying: "Who got rich during the goldrush? The pickaxe manufacturers." While it may be less flashy and less sexy to look at ancillary options, it is generally a wise choice. People who learned to safely pack and ship tulip bulbs were not suddenly out of business when tulip mania was over. They were able to transition their existing shipping companies into handling other cargo much more easily than someone who, after the prices fell, tried to recoup the money they had spent on bulbs. Almost every mania will feed a variety of industries that can exist without the mania itself. Think infrastructure, shipping, transportation, tools, education, etc.

- **It's natural to get distracted by shiny things. It's smart to design your business to withstand this tendency.** Entrepreneurs define ourselves by our creativity. How could we not? It's incredibly fun to come up with an idea, incubate it, and see it be born. As Salim Ismail and I discussed in our conversation (QR code in Chapter

Eleven), the entrepreneur's creativity, along with their willingness to take risks and break the rules, are what propel innovation. But often, because of the way our minds work, we've already moved onto the next thing before the first idea has come to fruition. This is far less enjoyable for everyone else inside your organization (your team and investors alike) who will suffer whiplash from your extreme twists and turns. As Ismail writes in his book *Exponential Organizations^*, organizations can only become exponential if they are designed in a way to withstand the entrepreneur's folly.

Chapter Thirteen

Plans and Port-a-potties

"A goal without a plan is just a wish."

—Anonymous proverb

Once there was an entrepreneur named Steve. Like many entrepreneurs, Steve liked to dabble in real estate. Steve and his wife bought a beautiful 1905 farmhouse in upstate New York that needed a lot of work. Between that fixer-upper, their primary residence, and the other properties they'd owned over the years, Steve had seen his fair share of contractors. Let's just say some were more organized than others.

Recently, Steve hired a contractor named Fred who showed up with blueprints and carefully thought-out plans. Most shockingly, Fred had a port-a-potty delivered. That port-a-potty spoke volumes.

Steve said to a friend, "I never thought I'd have strong opinions about a port-a-potty, but working with Fred made me realize something: if you don't bring a port-a-potty, you're planning to piss in the bushes. Even if you don't realize you're planning to piss in the bushes, you're leaving yourself no other choice."

Suddenly, it made no sense that many contractors and their teams had been crawling all over this property during former projects, and not once did they have a place to use the restroom. Except . . . you know.

So what's the equivalent of an E who's planning to piss in the bushes? An E who is paying expenses for the business due to negative cash flow, who is using OPM for their own big fat salary, doesn't have financial statements to prove their standing or their track record, or any or all of these.

A port-a-potty in this situation is a business blueprint, a.k.a. a well-thought-out plan on how the funds being raised are going to be used. This includes a clear plan for the return on the invested money and an exit strategy for the EI. These actions signal that an E isn't just fishing for OPM at the expense (literal and metaphorical) of the other person.

Fred having this amazing detail in place turned out to be the ultimate green flag in working with him. He was an excellent contractor in every way. Unfortunately, a leaking pipe (which had nothing to do with Fred) collapsed part of the ceiling, but I'll tell you, when Steve looked up there and saw Fred's wiring so nicely bundled and labeled, Steve was so impressed that he almost forgot he was looking through a hole in the ceiling.

Now Steve's perception has entirely changed. If a contractor showed up with a team of people for an eight-hour workday without a port-a-potty, Steve wouldn't have much faith in them. Similarly, once an EI has worked with an E who really has their shit together (no pun intended), they'll be far less inclined to invest in someone who doesn't.

Entrepreneurs don't need to be architects. You don't need to have the entire architecture for your future company planned out, but before you meet with potential investors, you do need to have some sort of road map to get you from Point A to Point B that demonstrates that you've thought through this opportunity. (If that sounds daunting, try a few guided-clarity blueprinting sessions that I offer in Pitchology to get clear on your concept and goals and figure out some next steps). A potential EI will be much more impressed if you show up with a port-a-potty.

Port-a-potty–level Green Flags

You may have guessed that the story above is from my own experience. Whether it's contractors with port-a-potties or Es who have prepared, here are some of the things I've learned to look for in a potential E that makes me confident they are not planning to piss in the bushes:

- **They've applied for IP rights.** Whether it's patents or trademarks, having done this shows they're serious.

- **They have a plan for raising capital.** All too often, entrepreneurs start out fundraising as a mission to get to a new place with their business. But unfortunately, they devolve to desperation because while fundraising, they stop focusing on their primary business. One solution to this issue is to have a person who points to potential investors and pitches them so the entrepreneur's focus can stay on the business.

- **They're already making money.** One of the best reasons to expand is that you have a purchase order in-hand, which you need capital to satisfy. Often an EI is more willing to invest in the opportunity of an already profitable idea than to fund a completely new idea.

- **They don't make potential investors jump through hoops to preview the pitch deck or video.** Don't make potential investors sign an NDA (non-disclosure agreement) out of the gate just to view your slide deck or have a conversation with you. EIs don't want to immediately engage in a legally binding document *before* getting a chance to decide whether or not they're interested in your idea. Assume the people you're approaching are busy. They don't want to have to enter their email address, create a username, or click a bunch of links to view your slide deck. Make it as easy as possible for them by sending it to them directly.

- **They have a good reputation.** If an EI reaches out to a mutual connection on a potential E's LinkedIn or through EO, and that connection gives a thumbs-up, that's a big green flag.

- **They have some sort of training, success, or expertise in a particular area.** This doesn't need to be a degree, but it can be. An advanced training or certification is also a good sign. Not only does it demonstrate their ability to stick with something long enough to finish it, but it can also point to expertise in a certain area.

- **They have previous capital from friends and family.** This is a green flag, but not having this is *not* a red flag. Not everyone comes from a family or social circle wealthy enough to invest. But if they *do* have capital from friends and family, that means that the E is willing to put their personal reputation on the line with their family, and the family believes in the E enough to invest.

Chapter Fourteen

Who are you sleeping with? —The Power of Vulnerability, Transparency, and Community

"It takes 20 years to build a reputation and five minutes to ruin it. If you think about that, you'll do things differently."

—Warren Buffett

Let me tell you a story about my good friend Dina. She's someone who has a good balance of intellect and intuition, which shows in both her thriving business and in her parenting.

She recently told me a story that has nothing to do with business . . . but it has everything to do with business, too.

Dina started dating a man. After several dates, she had fallen for him. Dina's two teenage kids from a previous marriage are at an age where it's not a whole process to introduce a new partner to them the way it would be for a small child, but still, Dina is selective about who she brings around her kids.

A few months into their relationship, Dina allowed the man to spend the night for the first time.

You can imagine her surprise when he climbed out of bed—nude—to walk to the bathroom and she immediately noticed an ankle monitor around his leg.

"What is that?" she asked.

"My ankle monitor. I'm required to be trackable by my parole officer for a ridiculous charge of fraud and embezzlement from a former employer," he said as casually as if he'd just mentioned getting coffee with a friend.

Dina thought she was dreaming. After the man left, she looked him up on the internet. Sure enough, he had been arrested and charged with embezzlement from his former place of employment.

Oh my God, she thought, he's a criminal.

This man went on numerous dates with her, pulled the wool over her eyes, and was audacious enough to come into her house where her children were sleeping, never having disclosed this piece of key information to her. The thing that disappointed Dina the most wasn't even that he had a criminal record, but that he had deceived her. That told her everything she needed to know about his character.

Needless to say, they broke up.

Know Thy Entrepreneurs

Now, let's think about EIs and Es.

An EI doesn't want to get to the point that they've invested a large sum of money with an E, and then after they've signed on the dotted line, they catch a glimpse of the ankle monitor. But sometimes that same passion that gets an E mesmerized by their own idea can spill over to the EI as well.

- **Don't get so mesmerized by someone else's energy that you don't perform due diligence.** Sometimes due diligence is a background check. Sometimes it's asking a friend for their input. Sometimes it's leaning into your networks. And sometimes, it means trusting your own gut above all else.

- **It's like a marriage.** The EI/E relationship is like dating in a lot of ways. Dynamics are important, and non-negotiable, for each party. Similar to how, at the beginning of your courtship with a prospective new romantic partner you might ask around your friend circle to see if anyone knows this person, before partnering with an E you should connect with investors or prior investors to understand their feelings about this person.

- **Use your networks**. You can learn a tremendous amount about a person through your various networks, even the free ones like LinkedIn. Some of the best places to verify a person's credibility are the following:

  - **EO (Entrepreneurs' Organization)** is a community where like-minded entrepreneurs can learn from one another to grow. Forums are an even smaller division of these communities which allow us to build strong relationships with 6–8 other EO members. EO allows us to be completely vulnerable with other entrepreneurs, which means we are held to a strict confidentiality understanding. We get to know each other well through vulnerability and highly value each others' experience shares.

- **YPO (Young Presidents' Organization)** is similar to EO but is also open to non-founders and management.

- **The Genius Network*** is an amazing group of entrepreneurs led by the charismatic entrepreneur, author, philanthropist, and addiction recovery advocate Joe Polish (a.k.a. The World's Most Connected Human).

- **Strategic Coach[1]** was founded and is led by entrepreneurial sage Dan Sullivan. This program brings order to the lives of many entrepreneurs and provides for a common language and structure to our lives and ventures.

- **A360** or **Abundance 360** is a community of founders, innovators, and serial entrepreneurs who collaborate on the cutting edge of innovation, from electric cars and space travel to longevity, health, technology, and more. This organization is led by Peter Diamandis, who is also a founder of the X Prize and Singularity University (to name a few). Participants commit to a 25-year journey of future exploration and create their Massive Transformative

Purpose. Members learn to connect their heads to their hearts in the work that they do.

- **LinkedIn** is one of the greatest tools for determining common connections and quickly identifying common relationships to verify someone's credibility. See who they're affiliated with and send messages to a few people. It will only take a few minutes, but you may be very glad you did!

- **Background checks** include both criminal *and* credit checks. Many people feel qualified to take an investment, even though their own finances are a trainwreck. Always remember, desperate people do desperate things. I run a background check on everyone we hire. If someone is going to manage millions or billions of dollars or they're going to have access to confidential information on people, they need to pass a background check.

- **A criminal record doesn't make someone inherently untrustworthy.** One of my most trusted financial advisors has a charge of theft on his record, but he was a sixteen-year-old who stole a candy bar. He let me know about it before I ran a background check, just so I wouldn't balk at the word "theft." Unlike Dina's new boyfriend, my financial advisor was forthright with this information out of respect for me and his profession. Transparency and vulnerability are key in building trust and avoiding being surprised in the future.

- **EIs want a well-orchestrated process.** The MOU should determine the interval of financial meetings. Agree upon monthly or even weekly calls on cash flow, upcoming requirements, additional business, and so on. These financials should typically be on an accrual basis, meaning that the expenses match the revenue that's being brought in. Go to <insert website location or QR code for the MOU builder.>

- **Trust and verify.** Energy is palpable. But some people can manipulate their energy, and therefore manipulate you. Typically, though, your gut will know. Some people call it their "Spidey Senses." And if all else fails, run a background check. That's not foolproof, but the best indicator of future behavior is past behavior, so sometimes it will be prudent.

- **Watch how they treat the busboy.** The entrepreneur community is quite small and we talk. Word travels quickly if there's something off about someone. And the things most of us are looking at aren't super impressive slide decks. We're watching how you treat other people. We're watching for signs that point to an E's character beyond the idea and beyond the potential investment.

- **Reputation is valuable.** If you jump into bed with the wrong person, you have their stink on you. The people we affiliate with are a reflection on our character.

Chapter Fifteen

Just Because it Moos Doesn't Mean You Can Milk It

"Nobody I know has ever enjoyed milking a bull, only the bull. Know where the milk ($) comes from!"

—Steve Distante

Once upon a time, a hungry wolf pup trotted out into a field of cows. He was worn out and desperate after having rummaged through garbage cans for scraps of food over the past few days. He knew that cows made milk and that milk was rich in the fat and

vitamins he needed to keep going until he reached Pigville, a place he'd heard to be very welcoming of wolves these days.

He gazed out over the animals grazing in the field. He spotted the biggest one. That one must make the most milk, he thought. The beast was enormous, with rippling muscles, and horns growing from its head. With his tail between his legs, the wolf pup approached the bull cautiously.

"Hey there little fella," said the bull in a deep voice. "Don't let the donkey see you or he'll chase you out of here."

"I was hoping you could give me some milk," said the wolf pup. "I'm very hungry."

The bull laughed, sending a cloud of black flies off of its back. "Oh, well I cannot help you there."

"Why not? Aren't you a cow?"

"I'm a bull," said the bull. "Don't you see how I'm different from all the rest of the herd?"

"It's true, I approached you first for being different," said the pup.

"I'm the biggest and strongest, yes. And yes, I do give life to the calves, who, in turn, cause their mothers to produce milk. But I do not have any milk for you. Ask around, though. I'm sure you'll find someone."

The pup scanned the rest of the bovines in the field. He saw another large one and went that direction.

"Well, hello there," said the steer, lowering his head to the pup's level.

"Hello," said the pup. "I'm looking for milk. Do you have any?"

The steer snorted, kicking up a cloud of dust from the ground. "Oh, not I. I serve my purpose here, but giving milk is not it. Tell me, why did you approach me and not the others for milk?"

The pup said, "Besides the bull, you're the biggest one out here."

The steer seemed proud to hear this. "I am, aren't I?"

The pup trotted on until he came upon a cow with a sway back and sharp hip bones. She turned out to be very old and told him she hadn't produced milk in several years.

The next cow he approached told him she would have milk soon, but it wasn't yet her season. The one after that said she had milk, but only enough for the calf that slept in the grass near her hooves. Before he left, once again discouraged, he heard a small voice say, "Hey wait!"

He looked around and saw a bright red cardinal perched on the cow's back.

"Me?" asked the wolf pup.

The cardinal fluttered to the ground in front of the pup's paws. "I've watched you going from cow to cow, not really knowing who has the milk you're looking for. And yeah, it's hit or miss. Some of them don't give milk at all, some of them will have it later, and some just ran out. But let me give you a hint. The ones who have milk will all walk to the barn the minute the farmer rings the bell. And that should happen any minute now."

"Why do they go to the barn?" asked the wolf pup.

"Because they're wanting to be milked!" said the cardinal.

"Really?" asked the wolf pup.

"Really," said the cardinal.

Sure enough, seconds later, a dinging rang out over the field, and the pup watched many of the cows lift their heads and begin walking to the barn. "Thank you!" he said to the bird, and went loping along with the cows.

Inside the barn, dozens of cows with swollen udders lined up to be milked. The pup found one who looked nice enough and asked yet again for some milk. This time, the cow nudged him with her nose and let him drink as much as he needed.

His belly full, the pup continued on his way to Pigville, where he ended up founding several successful businesses before he had his best idea yet. In seeking funding for his businesses, he was reminded of the day during his childhood when he'd gone from bull to steer to old cow to dry cow to mother cow, unable to find a sip of milk. When the cardinal tipped him off that the barn was where the cows went when they needed to be milked, he learned something valuable.

The pup decided to create a system where investors who had capital to invest could congregate, and hungry pups like himself could spend their time approaching potential matches and not waste anyone's time trying to milk a bull.

He called the place the Private Investor Network.

Join the Movement

Thank you for coming on this storytelling journey with me. It was certainly fun to write, and I hope it was equally as enjoyable to read. I hope some of these stories resonated with you. If, sometime in the future, you're in a situation and think of one of these characters, fables, or morals, I will consider this book to be a success.

If you're an E who's ready to find a mentor, investor, or both; or if you're an EI who's ready to fund a project or a person you believe in, then please join us at the PrivateInvestor.Network. The PIN is a place for EIs who find fulfillment through investing in fellow entrepreneurs and providing them with the capital they need to scale and grow . . . plus the bonus of exposure to the EI network and benefiting from their credibility.

The PIN is a place where Es who have exceptional ideas backed up by their natural drive can find the perfect investor/mentor.

In the magical land of Entrepreneurland, the EIs found their Es, the Es found their EIs . . .

~~And they all lived happily ever after.~~

And the rest was exponential.

Glossary of Terms

Driven[+] - a term coined by Dr. Doug Brackmann to describe an individual with the A1 allele on the DRD2 (dopamine receptor). These people are naturally driven to succeed, but if misdirected, this same nature can cause them to spiral into darkness.

E - my shorthand for "entrepreneur"

EI - my shorthand for "entrepreneur investor"

ELF* - Joe Polish's acronym for "easy, lucrative, and fun"

Entrepreneur's Organization - an international community of entrepreneurs that helps leaders grow their businesses and grow as individuals as well

ESOP - employee stock ownership plan

FOMO - fear of missing out

GRITT - the values I hold the most dearly, both for myself and for those I surround myself with: gratitude, respect, innovation, teamwork, and trustworthiness

HALF* - Joe Polish's acronym for "hard, annoying, lame, and frustrating"

Life's Work - the work that speaks to your soul. Everyone's Life's Work is different, but it's rarely about money (even if it makes money).

M&A - mergers and acquisitions

Magic Link - a questionnaire the PIN sends to an entrepreneur to help them evaluate their pitch. The Magic Link helps the E see shortcomings in their presentation (or in their idea) before presenting it to a potential EI.

MOU - The Memorandum of Understanding is a key element to a successful E/EI relationship. It sets the tone and expectations for the work the E and EI will do together. It is not binding, but can be expanded into a contract if needed.

NDA - non-disclosure agreement

NFT - non-fungible token

OPM - other people's money

PE - private equity (firm)

Private Investor Network - The **PIN** is the reason we're all here: the largest community of people ready to invest in each other!

R&D - research and development

Unique Ability - by definition, is the essence of what you love to do and do best. It's your own set of natural talents and the passion that fuels you to contribute in the ways that most motivate you. When articulated, it describes the "you" that makes you who you are.

VC - venture capitalist

Who, Not How[1] - a term first coined by Dean Jackson and expanded into a book (and theory) by Dan Sullivan and Dr. Benjamin Hardy. You can't possibly do everything yourself. Often, the key to success is finding the right Who, Not How[1] to get something done.

References

Aesop. "The Horse and the Groom." *Aesop Fables*. Daboss, November 2013.
https://fablesofaesop.com/the-horse-and-the-groom.html, accessed October 9, 2023.

Blanchard, Ken, Donald Carew and Eunice Parisi-Carew. *The One-Minute Manager Builds High Performing Teams*. New York, NY: HarperCollins, 1990.

Brackmann, Douglas PhD. Interview with Steve Distante (author).

[+]Brackmann, Douglas PhD and Randy Kelley. *Driven: Understanding and Harnessing the Genetic Gifts Shared by Entrepreneurs, Navy SEALs, Pro Athletes, and Maybe YOU.* Carson City, NV: Lioncrest Publishing, 2017.

Buffet, Warren. Quoted. in Dan Anderson, *Corporate Survival: The Critical Importance of Sustainability Risk Management*. Bloomington, IL: iUniverse, 2005, 138.

Burton, Wendy. Interview with Steve Distante, published in *Pitchology: The Art & Science of Raising Capital*. Seattle, WA: Impact U Press, 2023.

‡Collins, Jim and Jerry Porras. *Built to Last: Successful Habits of Visionary Companies*. New York, NY: HarperBusiness, 1994.

Disraeli, Benjamin. Widely attributed, source unknown.

Distante, Steve. *Pitchology: The Art & Science of Raising Capital*. Seattle, WA: Impact U Press, 2023.

Distante, Steve. Original quote from the author.

Gerber, Michael. *The E-Myth Revisited: Why Most Small Businesses Don't Work and What to Do About It*. New York, NY: Harper Collins 2009.

Ismail, Salim. Interview with Steve Distante (author).

^Ismail, Salim, Peter H. Diamandis, and Michael S. Malone. *Exponential Organizations 2.0: The New Playbook for 10x Growth and Impact*. Powell, OH: Ethos Collective, 2023.

Kay, Alan. Meeting of PARC (Palo Alto Research Center), 1971. Verified in email from Alan Kay to Peter W. Lount, September 17, 1998. Verbiage of email found here: https://quoteinvestigator.com/2012/09/27/invent-the-future/, accessed October 18, 2923.

Musk, Elon. Interview by Scott Pelley. *60 Minutes*, Season 44, Episode 26, March 18, 2012.

Polish, Joe. Interview with Steve Distante (author).

*Polish, Joe. *What's in It for Them?: 9 Genius Networking Principles to Get What You Want by Helping Others Get What They Want*. Carlsbad, CA: Hay House Business, 2023.

Robbins, Anthony. "Proximity is POWER." YouTube. Tony Robbins, August 15, 2022. https://www.youtube.com/watch?v=CVJ5xt96Pkw.

Rothschild, Baron Nathan. Widely attributed, source unknown.

Sinek, Simon. LinkedIn post, August 2023. https://www.linkedin.com/posts/simonsinek_do-you-want-to-be-the-leader-you-wish-you-activity-7091787894134099969-76Y0?utm_source=share&utm_medium=member_desktop, accessed October 18, 2023.

Santayana, George. *The Life of Reason, or The Phases of Human Progress*. New York, NY: Charles Scribner's Sons, 1905.

Sullivan, Dan. X (formerly Twitter) post, February 29, 2020. https://twitter.com/DanSullivanSC/status/1233814450521694210, accessed October 18, 2023.

[1]Sullivan, Dan and Dr. Benjamin Hardy. *Who, Not How: The Formula to Achieve Bigger Goals Through Accelerating Teamwork*. Carlsbad, CA: Hay House, 2020.

[2]Sullivan, Dan. What is Unique Ability®? Strategic Coach

Welch, Jack. quoted. in Julia Pimsleur, *Million Dollar Women: The Essential Guide for Female Entrepreneurs Who Want to Go Big*. New York, NY: Simon & Schuster, 2015, 199.